CW00751882

The AIMS Guide to

Your Rights in Pregnancy and Birth

An AIMS Publication

Principal Author: Emma Ashworth
AIMS Trustee

Published by AIMS
www.aims.org.uk
publications@aims.org.uk
Tel: 0300 365 0663

© AIMS 2020
Association for Improvements in the Maternity Services
Registered Charity Number 1157845
ISBN: 978-1-874413592

A catalogue record for this book is available from the British Library.

Printed in the Czech Republic by Printo

About AIMS

The Association for Improvements in the Maternity Services (AIMS) has been at the forefront of the childbirth movement since 1960. It is a volunteer-run charity and most of its work is carried out by volunteers without payment.

AIMS day-to-day work includes providing independent support and information about maternity choices and raising awareness of current research on childbirth and related issues. AIMS actively supports parents, midwives, doctors and birth workers who recognise that, for the majority of women, birth is a normal rather than a medical event. AIMS campaigns tirelessly on many issues covered by the Human Rights legislation.

AIMS campaigns internationally, nationally and locally for better births for all, protecting human rights in childbirth and the provision of objective, evidence-based information to enable informed decision making.

AIMS Mission

"We support all maternity service users to navigate the system as it exists, and campaign for a system that truly meets the needs of all."

AIMS Equality, Diversity and Inclusivity Statement

AIMS Equality, Diversity and Inclusivity Statement is available on the AIMS website at *www.aims.org.uk/general/aims-equality-diversity-and-inclusivity-statement.*

AIMS promotes equality, values diversity and challenges discrimination and with this statement we make a commitment to do so irrespective of characteristics. Freedom of expression is fundamental to AIMS and we will endeavour to publish diverse voices and wide-ranging opinions.

AIMS will work towards ensuring that all our written works will be made available in a variety of formats to meet different needs and that the language is inclusive to all.

AIMS wishes to support everyone throughout their pregnancy, ensuring that they are protected, included, celebrated and retain autonomy over their bodies.

Acknowledgements

Although I was the principal author of this book, I am indebted to many people for their help and advice and the knowledge that they have shared. Like all AIMS publications, this book has benefited immensely from the critical comments and suggestions of a group of AIMS Volunteers. It is this approach, drawing on the knowledge and insight of both clinical and lay readers, that ensures that AIMS books meet the needs of our main audience, the individual maternity service user, as well as providing valuable information to those who support them. I simply could not have written this book without you all.

Shane Ridley, Virginia Hatton, Verina Henchy, Deborah Rhodes, Deborah Neiger, Samantha Gadsden, Seána McCoy Talbot, Nadia Higson, Veronica Blanco, Winsa Dai, Debbie Chippington Derrick, Alison Little, Gillian Weaver, Maria Booker, Rachel Boldero, Kay King, Philippa Rumary, Kristina Bloedorn, Anne Glover, Naomi Tolson, Lucy Williamson, Katie Fountain, Anita Kolaczynska, Nicola Enoch, Justine Fieth, Mari Greenfield and Julie Ann Crowley.

Thank you to these amazing organisations who have provided assistance in the book's writing or invaluable information for signposting:

Birthrights
The Miscarriage Association
Sands
Tommy's
Bliss

I would like to offer a very special thank you to our patient editor, Alison Melvin, who also typeset the manuscript. I could not have written this book without your expertise. A big thank you to Chloe Bayfield, former AIMS

Trustee, for proofreading, and our printer in the Czech Republic, Daniel Zabek.

Finally, and most importantly, I would like to thank my family. My wonderful, ever-supportive husband, Philip, without whom I would not be able to do the work that I am so passionate about, and our gorgeous, wonderful sons, Peter, Toby and Jacob, who have been incredibly patient with me throughout the writing of this book. And my Mum, Wendy, a wonderful midwife who raised me to be a feminist, an activist and to love birth. Thank you all.

Contents

Introduction

Being pregnant and giving birth will lead you into a healthcare environment where you will be asked to make lots of decisions – about your own care, about your birth and about your baby. This book helps you to navigate the maternity system and to understand your rights in pregnancy and birth, and it gives you tools to help you to assert those rights and make decisions that are right for you.

We hope that there will be lots of information that you find really useful, but the one thing we would like you to take away is that:

Your Body is Your Own

You are the only person who can make decisions about what happens to *your* body. Being pregnant does NOT change that. If you are told that "you have to" have a test, check or intervention, whether that's when you are pregnant, while you're giving birth or after your birth, please know that it's up to you to accept or decline it. Of course, you can seek other people's advice or opinions, but you are the one who can say "yes" or "no".

There are many aspects of UK law that come together to offer protection to everyone when it comes to their own body autonomy, and these continue to apply to pregnant women and people. Many but not all of these will be touched on in this book, but whatever happens to you on your pregnancy, birth and postnatal journey, remember that it's you who calls the shots. It's your body, your baby and it's you who gets to make the decisions.

Some people decide that they want to follow the advice of their midwife or doctor without delving more deeply into the pros and cons of that advice.

That is also in your power to decide. You don't have to make every decision yourself if you don't want to – that in itself is your decision!

In the UK there is only one situation where a pregnant or birthing woman or person may not be able to make some decisions for themselves. This is when they do not have 'capacity'. Capacity as a legal term is explained in Chapter 1 (p.7). There are clear legal protections for everyone so that a doctor cannot simply decide that a person doesn't have capacity and then make decisions for that person other than in very specific situations, such as if the person is unconscious. Even then, there are limits on what the doctor can do.

How the law impacts on your rights is different around the world and even within the four countries that make up the United Kingdom, so it is important for you to read this book but also to obtain any legal advice you might need, if this is necessary. This book is not intended to give legal advice.

Problems with the law

As you read this book you will find that it frequently refers to the fact that anyone who performs a test, treatment or intervention on your body without your informed consent, given freely and without coercion, is committing assault and battery, which is a criminal offence. However, it has been AIMS experience that the police may be unwilling to take a case where someone has been assaulted by medical staff. This is something that some birth campaigners are working to change. While the law is clear, the way that the law is upheld in this and other related areas (for instance, within family law courts) is not always so clear.

Having said that, it can be extremely helpful to remind people of the law and how it is designed to protect you. Very often, knowing your rights and asserting them will stop any coercive or abusive behaviour, and this book will help you to understand those rights.

How to get the best out of this book – an explanation of its structure

We suggest that you read the whole book to get an overall impression of the maternity services and how they work. You will then be able to pick up anything that might be an issue for you as you go through your pregnancy and you can refer back to the specific chapters.

Links to online information and websites

Throughout this book you will see that all signposts, links and references have the same web address: *aims.org.uk/rights*. We have listed all of the signposts, links and references for the book on this web page. This means that they can be regularly checked to ensure that they are up to date and accurate.At the top of this web page is a list of links to each of the pages in the book that have a signpost, link or reference. Click on the page number of the book that you're on and it will take you to the reference that is on that page. The Kindle version will take you directly to the correct reference automatically.

Chapter synopsis

Chapter 1 introduces the concepts of capacity and consent. These concepts are key to understanding your rights, and the power that you have to decide on what happens during your pregnancy and birth.

Chapter 2 explains who's who in maternity care, and what their roles are so that you know who you might see, or who you can reach out to if you need specific help or care. It explains all the groups of staff that you might come across in your pregnancy and birth journey, together with a brief overview of how health care is organised. In addition, the issue of 'safeguarding' is referred to with signposts to more help should you need it.

Chapter 3 offers some techniques for gathering information and knowledge so you can make an informed decision. Once you understand your rights to make decisions, the next step is to have some tools that you can use to assert those rights.

Chapter 4 is an important chapter that outlines the obligations that all healthcare providers are under to give you good care. There are many rules, guidelines and standards that your carers must follow and although this book cannot mention them all, we aim to signpost you to them. The chapter goes into more detail about your rights, about how to consent to or decline treatment and how to recognise when you are being coerced to do something against your better judgment. The final section provides information about how to make a complaint if you have experienced poor care.

What to expect from your antenatal care and the screening and tests you may be offered are discussed in Chapters 5 and 6.

Chapter 7 first explains how your birth space can influence your body's production of oxytocin. When you understand how important this hormone is, then you will understand the importance of your birth environment.

Chapter 8 leads you to the time approaching your baby's birth and examines the whys and wherefores of your due date and the consequences that follow in the form of the pressure that you might be under to induce your labour.

Chapter 9 reiterates the rights you have during your labour. Although we don't suggest you read the book whilst you are in labour, it might be helpful to have it with you and share it with your birth partner!

Chapter 10 reminds you of your choices regarding cutting the cord, birthing your placenta and, so importantly, how to spend that special time with your baby often known as the 'Golden Hour'. Breastfeeding and how it can protect a baby from illness is explained here, and there are tests for your baby for you to consider too. We also give the administrative information for notifying the birth and registering your baby.

The final section of the book offers help and support to those who experience the loss of their pregnancy, or the death of their baby. This section is here solely to offer support and information for those who need it. There is no need to read this if it doesn't apply to you, unless you want to. If you do need this section, we are so sorry that you have lost your baby. We hope that having this information in one place helps to offer some support to you at this time.

The AIMS Guide to Your Rights in Pregnancy and Birth is also a handbook for those working in any part of the maternity services, for birth workers and anyone supporting women and pregnant people through pregnancy, birth and beyond.

Language

AIMS understands that there is a huge diversity of people who use the maternity services. AIMS seeks to support all users, so we have tried to make the language in this book inclusive. Much of the time we use 'you' – directed at the reader who will usually be the maternity service user. We use the words mothers or women when these are the words used by authors of research or guidelines. Elsewhere we have used a mix of women, mothers, people, or pregnant women and people. AIMS has an Equality, Diversity and Inclusivity Statement, which you can read at the front of this book.

General information

Guidelines are often referred to throughout the book. The professional bodies that regulate midwives and doctors are the Royal College of Midwives (RCM) and the Royal College of Obstetricians and Gynaecologists (RCOG) and they regularly publish guidance notes to aid good clinical practice. They do not dictate a single solution and the responsibility for your care still lies with the individual practitioner. You can find many examples of maternity guidelines on their websites *www.rcm.org.uk* (Blue Top Guidance) and *www.rcog.org.uk* (Green Top Guidance).

NICE (The National Institute for Health and Care Excellence) develop recommendations using the best available evidence to publish guidance in a number of areas – you might have heard of them in relation to their advice on the use of medicines. There are many guidelines about maternity care which can be found on their website *www.nice.org.uk*.

You will see references throughout the book to the Birth Information page to be found at *www.aims.org.uk/information/page/1*. This page is intended to provide useful information on a variety of topics and particularly those that are frequently asked about on the AIMS helplines. This information is not intended to replace medical advice, but instead to help people to work out what questions they may wish to ask their healthcare providers to help them to make their own decisions.

Finally, the book points the way to people and organisations who offer support. Remember that AIMS email and phone helplines are also there if you need them, *helpline@aims.org.uk* and +44 (0) 300 3650663. This phone number will connect you to an AIMS Volunteer when possible, otherwise please leave us a message, or email us, and someone will get back to you.

About the principal author

Emma Ashworth is a birth researcher and writer. She has been a women's rights activist and feminist for nearly 30 years, and a birth rights activist for over 15 years. She is also a doula and breastfeeding counsellor, AIMS Trustee and AIMS Volunteer. Emma is passionate about ensuring that women and people know their rights in pregnancy and birth, and that they know that they are the only ones who can make decisions about their own bodies. Emma is very happily married to the ever-supportive Philip, and they have three amazing children – Peter, Toby and Jacob.

Chapter 1

Capacity and Consent

'Capacity', when used in a legal context, refers to the ability of a person to make decisions for themselves. The reason that capacity is explained at the beginning of this book is because when a person is offered any medical treatment they are free to decide whether to give their consent to it or to decline it, provided they have the 'capacity' to do so. The NHS states that,

> 'All adults are presumed to have sufficient capacity to decide on their own medical treatment, unless there's significant evidence to suggest otherwise.'

There are strict rules that have to be followed if a person is deemed to *not* have the capacity to make a decision for themselves. This chapter explains when this might happen, so that you can understand that in all other situations it is you, and you alone, who makes the decisions about your body. 'Consent' is also explained in this chapter, so that you know what is legally required of doctors, midwives and other healthcare providers when they are providing you with care.

Capacity to make decisions

The NHS explains that a person may not have capacity if they cannot:

- understand information about a decision and
- remember that information and
- use that information to make a decision and
- communicate their decision by talking, using sign language or any other means.

You can read the NHS web page on capacity via this link: *aims.org.uk/rights*.

Very rarely, a healthcare professional may have serious doubts that a pregnant woman or person has the capacity to make a decision about a specific treatment or intervention. In this case, a doctor can appeal to the Court of Protection for a legal ruling which, if given, means that the pregnant woman or person loses the right to accept or decline that specific treatment or intervention.

Capacity is decided on an issue by issue basis, which means that a court order will only apply to specific decisions and the pregnant woman or person will retain the right to make all other decisions. For example, if a court order states that a woman does not have the capacity to make a decision on whether or not she has a caesarean birth, she may still be able to decide whether she wishes to breastfeed and she may have control over other decisions around the birth, such as whether she has immediate skin to skin with her baby, depending on her capacity to make these decisions.

In an emergency situation, where, unexpectedly, the person giving birth does not have the capacity to make a decision and cannot give consent for urgent treatment, the doctor who is treating that person will be responsible for making a decision about what is in their patient's best interests. An example of this would be if a labouring woman is unconscious and unable to communicate but is at risk of harm if an intervention isn't done immediately. In this situation, the doctor would be required to follow strict guidance, which would normally include obtaining information from people who are close to the woman about what her preferences may be, or reading her preferences in a birth plan. However, the person providing the health care is responsible for making the final decision on what to do in this situation.

A person cannot 'lose capacity', they can only lose capacity to make a specific decision or set of decisions. A red flag would be if a healthcare provider claimed that a *person* did not have capacity as it shows that they are not recognising that, legally, a person's capacity to make a decision must be considered for each decision that needs to be made – it cannot be a blanket statement about a person.

If a doctor decides that a woman or person does not have capacity to make a decision, the doctor is at risk of legal consequences if it is later found that appropriate procedures were not followed. Legal consequences may include having a case brought against them for malpractice, a criminal assault and battery charge, and possible removal of their ability to practise. They would have to be extremely sure of their position to decide that a woman or person does not have capacity to make a decision without the backing of a court order.

It is important to note that a doctor cannot decide that someone does not have the capacity to give their consent solely because the doctor disagrees with their decision, or because they think that it is irrational.

AIMS does not give legal advice, and the information in this section is solely designed to give readers an overview of the law on capacity. If you would like or need to know more about capacity, please contact a specialist lawyer or Birthrights. Birthrights' website can be found via this link: *aims.org.uk/rights*.

For the purposes of this book it is assumed that you have the capacity to make your own decisions.

The meaning of consent

Health care is offered to us in the form of a test, a drug, an operation or another type of intervention and we can choose to accept the offer or decline it. It is optional, not mandatory, even if declining the offer could harm you or your unborn baby, or even lead to your death or the death of your unborn baby.

Any offer of health care must come with an explanation of why it's offered, what the benefits and risks of it are, and what other options there might be, including doing nothing. The conversation should include what's important to you, and be personalised to your needs. You should then be given the time to make a decision, and your decision must, by law, be respected. While some decisions may have a natural time limit, such as in genuine birth emergencies, it is almost always the case that there will be some time to think, process, research and, if you wish, to ask more questions. It is important to know that you can have more time to talk and to think about your decision if you want it.

Healthcare providers sometimes talk about 'consenting patients'. For example, they may say "I'm going to go and consent Mrs Jones", or "Can you consent Miss Smith?" This implies that Mrs Jones or Miss Smith will simply go along with what they are told is going to happen. However, consent can only be given at the end part of a process of full discussion and information sharing. This process gives the pregnant woman or person information about what is on offer, enabling them to consent to it or decline it. It must involve offering a clear explanation of the general advantages and disadvantages of the intervention and the risks and benefits as they apply to that individual. It should cover whether the offer is evidence-based, or based on opinion, and how strong the evidence is. It should also cover what other options might be available. The pregnant woman or person can then consider this information, make their decision and their decision must be respected. If a consent form is signed without this process happening, then even though there may be a signature on a form, informed consent cannot be said to have been given. See also Chapter 3 (p.24) and the AIMS web page on consent: *aims.org.uk/rights*.

A good summary of consent is that:

- **It must be voluntary**; it is your decision alone, given without coercion, undue influence or persuasion from anyone else. 'Anyone else' includes partners and other family members and friends, not just midwives and doctors.
- **It must be informed**; you must have all the information you need to give consent.
- **It must be given freely for it to be legal.** If consent is only given because of coercion or a threat, it is not given freely and therefore not legal.

Consent may be given:

- **orally;** for instance, you may say "Yes, OK".
- **in writing**; you might sign a consent form, for example.
- **with your body language;** for instance you might roll up your sleeve and offer your arm for a blood test.

However, in all cases **informed consent** is not considered given unless you have all the information you need to make your decision.

Equally, consent can be declined:

- **orally;** you may say, "no" or "stop", for example.
- **in writing;** you can write that you do not consent to something.
- **with your body language;** for instance you may close your legs to decline a vaginal examination, or push someone away.

Consent can be withdrawn (stopped) at any time, even if you have given your consent in writing.

This book aims to talk you through your rights in pregnancy, birth and early parenthood, to help you to feel confident in deciding what's right for you and to ensure that you know that any decisions you may need to make in pregnancy, during your birth and after your birth are yours; they are not the doctor's, midwife's or anyone else's. It is not up to someone else to 'allow' or 'not allow' you.

Chapter 2

An introduction to maternity services

This chapter explains the different roles within the maternity services so that you have information about who is out there to help and support you with your rights in pregnancy and birth. There is also a brief explanation of Children's Services and about how health care is organised in the UK, and there is signposting to more information about your employment rights, maternity benefits and access to the NHS.

Midwives

Everyone who is pregnant should be able to access care from a midwife. (See 'Booking with a midwife' on page 59 for more information.) A midwife's expertise is in supporting straightforward pregnancy, birth and the early postnatal period, as well as in having a high level of skill in detecting complications and providing support to deal with them.

Even if a pregnant woman or person has an extremely complex pregnancy, a midwife will still be available as part of the care team if the woman or person wants one. A midwife will refer people in their care to a specialist midwife (e.g. a diabetes midwife or to an obstetrician) if they feel that they may benefit from additional medical care but no one is obliged to accept this referral if they don't want it.

Midwives will have some training in breastfeeding support, and some may have taken additional training courses and have a higher level of expertise. However, breastfeeding support is its own specialist area and, for many breastfeeding problems, a specialist such as a breastfeeding counsellor (BFC) or International Board Certified Lactation Consultant (IBCLC) will be better able to help.

Some midwives have the title Consultant Midwife. These midwives have far more influence on the services offered in their area so they can be a helpful person to reach out to if your own midwife isn't supporting you to access the services you want.

Head of Midwifery (HoM)

The Head of Midwifery is responsible for the midwives in the hospital and the management of the midwifery team. They also have a role in supporting individual woman and people's specific needs. Some Heads of Midwifery can be extremely supportive when it comes to seeking care outside of guidelines or in unusual circumstances. You can contact them by asking your midwife for their email address or phone number, or calling the hospital's reception for this information. Sometimes it will be on the hospital's website.

Professional Midwifery Advocates (PMA)

The PMA is a midwife who has taken on additional responsibilities that should include being an advocate for women and their decisions. If your birth plan, or your decisions in pregnancy or soon after birth are not being supported by your midwife, you can contact the PMA.

All hospitals should have PMAs and their contact details on their website. Or you can phone the labour ward, or your own midwife, to ask for their contact information.

Maternity Support Workers (MSW)

MSWs assist midwives to offer care to people who are pregnant, giving birth or who have recently given birth. They are not there to replace a midwife but to provide additional support and care.

Doulas

Doulas are sometimes employed by the hospital, but are usually employed privately by individual pregnant women and people. They offer a wide range of non-clinical support to both the person who is pregnant and their wider family. They may be able to help you to plan your birth, to signpost you to information, to help with advocacy when you are interacting with midwives and doctors, and to offer practical, physical and emotional support during the birth of your baby. While doulas may also be qualified midwives, they are not allowed to offer you clinical midwifery care in your labour unless they are currently on the register of midwives with the Nursing and Midwifery Council (NMC), and in that case they must also have appropriate indemnity insurance. A doula may attend your birth without a midwife or doctor being there as well, if you want, but they can't act as a midwife or doctor. The term 'doula' is not a protected term, which means that anyone can say they're a doula, whether they have done any training or not, so you may wish to talk to them about what experience or training they have if that is important to you.

If you would like to know more about doulas, a good site to start with is Doula UK. See the link in *aims.org.uk/rights*. They have a list of doulas near you and you can read more about the services doulas offer and get an idea of the prices they charge. Importantly they advise how to choose a doula.

Obstetricians

An obstetrician is a doctor who specialises in the care of pregnant and birthing people. They are trained to provide medical and surgical interventions for pregnancy and birth-related health conditions and emergencies, but may have less knowledge than a midwife or doula about how to support women and people to help their own bodies to work most effectively in their pregnancy and birth. If you have an obstetrician as part of your care team, you should also be able to have a midwife if you want one.

Your obstetrician should be liaising with your own consultant if you have any chronic health conditions.

Obstetric Anaesthetists

During your pregnancy, you may be offered an appointment with an anaesthetist, who should discuss pain relief and anaesthetic choices for your labour and birth. They will give you an epidural if you have asked for one.

Obstetric Physiotherapists

Obstetric physiotherapists specialise in the physical changes to your body that pregnancy and childbirth can bring. Specifically, they may run the Pelvic Girdle Pain (PGP) clinic for people suffering pain in one or more of the three pelvic joints during their pregnancy. Those who have had an instrumental birth, a serious tear or a caesarean section can be referred for advice on postnatal exercises to aid recovery. Specialist physiotherapists may belong to the Pelvic Obstetric and Gynaecological Physiotherapy Network (POGP). Sometimes this is available on the NHS, but waiting lists are often long, so some women and people prefer to seek out private practitioners.

Neonatal Paediatricians

A neonatal paediatrician is a doctor who specialises in the care of newly-born babies. If your baby is healthy you are unlikely to see a paediatrician. However, a paediatrician may do the 'newborn baby check' although in many cases a midwife will provide this check (see page 140 on the newborn baby check, NIPE).

Neonatal Nurses

Nurses who look after babies who are born prematurely or unwell are also in the Maternity Care Team. Most neonatal nurses work in SCBU (Special Care Baby Unit) or NICU (Neonatal Intensive Care Unit). If your baby is healthy and well you are unlikely to see a neonatal nurse.

Health Visitors (HV)

The Health Visitor service offers child health and development support to parents. Once you are signed off by the midwifery service you will be offered a variety of services from the HV. In addition, HVs will usually offer a home visit before your baby is born to introduce themselves and to talk through any questions that you might have about caring for your new baby. Part of the purpose of this antenatal visit is safeguarding, so the health visitor will be looking for signs that the family is providing a safe environment. In addition to home visits, HVs usually run clinics, which may be available as a walk-in clinic or they may have a booking system. These can be a useful resource for getting your baby weighed or checked, if you have any concerns, and to talk about any issues you may be experiencing.

The HV service is available until your child is of compulsory education age, when the school nurse takes over that role. The school nurse is also available to children who are educated outside of school.

Infant Feeding Specialists

There are three main qualifications for infant feeding specialists:

Breastfeeding Peer Supporters (sometimes known as Mother Supporters) learn to support normal breastfeeding and common breastfeeding issues. Ideally, peer/mother supporters will have trained with regionally recognised organisations, or with one of the four national breastfeeding charities (see below). Some will have been trained by the local hospital where the training can be excellent, but is sometimes of a lower standard. They can be an invaluable resource for helping women to deal with straightforward breastfeeding challenges. Peer supporters are usually volunteers in the community, and some are employed by the NHS. Peer supporters should also have training in supporting formula feeding and mix feeding (part breastfeeding, part formula feeding).

Breastfeeding Counsellors in the UK are trained by one of four organisations: NCT, ABM (The Association of Breastfeeding Mothers), BfN (Breastfeeding Network) or LLL (La Leche League). They have completed an in-depth course which includes the biology of breastfeeding, practical skills for supporting both normal breastfeeding and for overcoming some of the problems that can occur and counselling skills. This training is significantly more than that offered as standard to midwives and health visitors, and takes around two years of part-time study to complete. Breastfeeding counsellors are usually volunteers or private practitioners, but occasionally they are employed by the NHS. Breastfeeding counsellors should also be able to offer support with formula feeding and mix feeding.

International Board Certified Lactation Consultants (IBCLC). An IBCLC is often also a health professional, such as a nurse or midwife (but doesn't have to be), and has completed around 1,000 hours in practice (depending on the training pathway) and passed written examinations. They usually work as volunteers or private practitioners, and are occasionally employed by the NHS.

The terms 'peer supporter', 'mother supporter' and 'breastfeeding counsellor' are unprotected in law, meaning that anyone can refer to themselves with these terms, so it's always worth asking whether the person you are seeing has been trained by one of the main charities and has a recognised certification from them.

If you are seeking support for infant feeding you might prefer to reach out to the main UK charities for information on who is local to you. You can find a list of the charities which train breastfeeding counsellors, and the UK's listings of IBCLCS, via this link *aims.org.uk/rights*, or on the Kindle version via these links: ABM, NCT, BfN, LLL, Lactation Consultants Great Britain.

Interpreters and Translators

While interpreters and translators are not part of the maternity staff team, we have included them in this section as they are a critical part of some people's maternity care.

For a person to make an informed decision, they need to have properly understood the information that they have received. For this reason, the NHS states that

> 'Patients should be able to access primary care services in a way that ensures their language and communication requirements do not prevent them receiving the same quality of health care as others.'

It is advisable to speak to your midwife or doctor about arranging appropriate translation or interpreting services well in advance of your birth. Hospitals and other healthcare services are not permitted to charge patients for the use of this service.

If you wish, you can have your partner, friend or support person interpret or translate for you. However, NHS best practice states that this should not be recommended and that you should have another interpreter or translator speak to you first, independently of anyone else, so you can state your preference in private.

For more information, see the NHS guidance via this link: *aims.org.uk/rights*.

Children's Services

Children's Services is the section of Social Services that focuses on the health and welfare of children. Those working in the service are called social workers. They can become involved if there are concerns that an unborn baby might be at risk *after* birth.

Some families find that their social worker is extremely valuable, providing them with helpful advice and support. Social workers should be supporting families and, where possible, helping them to stay together. However, it is extremely important that you seek help immediately if you are referred to Children's Services, or if you are threatened with a referral to them, because sometimes families can find themselves in serious difficulties. Seeking help early can often resolve issues quickly before they escalate. We strongly urge you to contact the AIMS helpline where we can also provide you with information and support. See *aims.org.uk/rights*.

For more information about being referred to Children's Services, see 'The right for the pregnant woman or person to decide what happens to their body' in Chapter 4 (p. 37). We also recommend that you read *The AIMS Guide to Resolution after Birth, Chapter 6.*

How health care is organised in the countries of the UK

Health care is devolved, meaning that there are quite significant differences between the way that the health systems are run in each of the four countries of the UK, even though they are all branded 'NHS'.

England

NHS England is broken down into multiple areas, each of which is given its own budget to run health services. This budget is managed by Clinical Commissioning Groups, or CCGs. You can see a map of the CCGs in England here, *aims.org.uk/rights*.

The CCGs use this budget to 'buy' the health services that are needed to support the local community. In practice the organisations that the CCG buys most maternity services from are the CCG's local NHS Hospital Trusts. Trusts are, effectively, not for profit businesses that supply services to local residents, paid for by the CCG. A Trust may run one or more hospitals, as well as services such as Community Midwifery and Health Visiting, and you will see their names on much of the local NHS branding, such as 'North Lincolnshire and Goole NHS Foundation Trust'.

NHS maternity care is most likely to be managed from the hospital that is closest to where you live. Sometimes, there may be a service that you want to access which is offered by your neighbouring Trust; there might be a lovely birth centre there, for example, or you may not want to go back to the hospital where you had a bad experience. You should be able to book with and access the services of neighbouring Trusts, or transfer your care there if you have already booked in with your midwife. You may experience some resistance to this because of the paperwork involved, and your local Trust will lose the funding they receive for you; however, it is normally possible. It is usually better to approach the Trust that you want to book with rather than ask your closest Trust to arrange this. If you are planning a homebirth, you may have to book with the Trust which is nearest to you as the homebirth midwives may not be able to travel to you from another Trust.

Wales

Wales has a similar Trust system to England, and if you want to book with a hospital in a Trust which doesn't cover the area in which you live, you can ask to do this.

Scotland

Scotland has Health Boards. There are 14 regional Health Boards and each of those have a number of Health and Social Care Partnerships (HSCPs). As in England and Wales, you don't have to book with your nearest hospital, although geographically other hospitals may be too far away to access practically. For homebirth services, you may need to be with the service nearest to you.

Northern Ireland

In Northern Ireland there are five Local Commissioning Groups (LCGs), which are overseen by the Health and Social Care Board (HSCB) and the Public Health Agency (PHA). Pregnant women and people in Northern Ireland may choose whichever hospital they like within the country, although for homebirth services you may need to book with the service nearest to you.

Employment rights, maternity benefits and accessing the NHS

Everyone who is pregnant and entitled to NHS care is entitled to free dental care and free prescriptions, throughout their pregnancy and for a year after birth. In order to access this free care it is necessary to apply for a Maternity Exemption Certificate. Your midwife, doctor or health visitor should give you the form (FW8) to apply for this. This form can only be completed by a registered midwife, doctor or health visitor.

In order to claim Statutory Maternity Pay from an employer, or, if you do not qualify for this, Maternity Allowance from the Jobcentre, you need to ask a midwife, doctor or health visitor to complete the form MAT B1. You can access the UK Government's information on the MAT B1 form via *aims. org.uk/rights*.

More information on maternity pay is available from the UK Government's website via *aims.org.uk/rights*.

It is illegal for employers to discriminate against a woman because she is pregnant, and pregnant women have certain rights in law which help to protect them. The right to this protection applies to everyone, including contract workers, from the day that they are employed. While the language used in the law refers to women, the law should still apply to trans men, non-binary people and other pregnant people. The charity Maternity Action has more information on discrimination during maternity leave and The Citizen's Advice Bureau also has helpful information: *aims.org.uk/rights*.

Entitlement to NHS care

In the UK, in an emergency, anyone who is pregnant has the right to care, whether or not they are entitled to NHS care. Individuals who are not entitled to free NHS care cannot be denied care in an emergency, nor be told that they will have to pay before care is given. Afterwards, those without the right to free care from the NHS may be asked to pay, depending on the circumstances.

This situation is complex, and depends on factors such as the person's immigration status, and there are groups who may be entitled to free care but are unaware that they are. It is therefore important to seek advice from a trained advocate. The charity Maternity Action has helpful information on their website, as well as a helpline where they signpost to groups dedicated to supporting individuals' specific situations, which you can access via *aims. org.uk/rights*. The UK Government's website also has information – see *aims. org.uk/rights*.

Chapter 3

Information gathering and decision making

This chapter gives you some decision-making tools to help you to work out **what's right for you**. These can be applied to anything that you are offered during your pregnancy and your birth and for all aspects of medical care. We offer some techniques for gathering and acquiring the information and knowledge you might need, and some methods of using the information to make your decisions.

You can read and refer back to the decision making section (page 31) to help you through each specific situation. It offers tried and tested techniques to help you to assert your rights and navigate the maternity system.

If you have already decided to decline an intervention, test or treatment, you don't need to have these conversations if you don't want to (this is further explained in the following chapter, Chapter 4). However, if you want to gather information first and then make a decision, these tools will help. The AIMS Birth Information page, 'Making decisions about your maternity care' may be a helpful reference to read as well. See *aims.org.uk/rights*.

Gathering information and acquiring knowledge

Be very clear about what you want to achieve

It can help to state what is important to you very clearly, and ask how this can be achieved – focusing on solutions, not problems, and asking the midwife or doctor to do so as well. If you are not getting the support you need, you can ask for a complete list of the reasons why what you want to happen is being rejected. You can then address those points one by one – although of course you don't normally have to do this there and then. By focusing on your goal, and understanding what the barriers are, you have something concrete to work with. Otherwise you might find yourself being side-tracked by vague but emotive comments along the lines of "you're putting yourself/your baby at risk" – or by non-reasons.

What are non-reasons? Sometimes, the reasons that we are given to explain why something is being denied are not reasons at all. Some examples might be, "Health and safety reasons", "Because your BMI is too high/low", "Medico-legal reasons". Sometimes it might be, "We just want you and baby to be safe". These are not explanations. They are non-answers. They do not give you the information that you need to make your decision.

It is absolutely fine to dig deeper into these reasons and ask for more explanation.

For instance, you could say, "Could you please explain why my BMI means that you want me to have that intervention? What outcomes are you concerned about that my BMI may affect and how does this compare with people with a higher/lower BMI? What are the chances, in numbers, that this outcome might happen solely because of my BMI? What is the evidence that supports your advice on this issue?"

Or you could say, "Can you explain in exactly what way the choice I've made might affect my, or someone else's, health or safety. What evidence is this based on?"

You can ask the midwife or doctor to tell you what options there are to overcome the barriers to the care that you want, and you can also offer your own solutions to the problem, which the doctor or midwife does have to consider thoroughly. Depending on the situation and the amount of time you have, you might find it best to have these discussions in writing or, at the very least, to record the conversation (see next section).

On the other side of the coin, you may find that the midwife or doctor attempts to blind you with science. Rather than offering a non-explanation, they may try to give you more information than you can reasonably process or understand. This is where recording the discussion may help, so that you can go over it again later, possibly with another midwife or doctor. You could also say, "I don't understand what you just said. Could you explain it again, please." Or, "That's too much information for me to take in right now. Can you tell me the most important parts so I can think about those, and then I'll come back to you another time for the rest." The important thing to know is that if you feel that you need information to be given to you more slowly, or in a different way, or maybe in a different format (e.g. in writing) then this is what needs to happen.

In summary, you do not have to take what is said to you at face value. You are absolutely entitled to have an explanation that makes sense to you, and which is backed up by evidence. If an 'explanation' doesn't explain anything then it's not an explanation at all.

Recording conversations

Consultations with medical staff can sometimes be very daunting, especially if the pregnant woman or person has felt bullied by medical staff in the past.

It can also be difficult to remember all of the details of a conversation if you are faced with a lot of facts and figures or if you are feeling anxious. Recording a conversation with a midwife or doctor can be very beneficial for both of these reasons: it can help to ensure that the midwife or doctor is careful about how they talk to you and their obligation to give impartial information, and that you can listen to the explanation again so that you don't forget important details. If you are asked why you want to record the conversation you can just say that you want to be able to remember the details later. The more people who ask to record consultations, the more it will become common practice.

The Medical Defence Union (MDU) has useful information on recording consultations. It states that patients are legally allowed to record their consultations, and that a medical practitioner's duty of care means that they would not be justified in refusing to continue with the consultation if they did not want to be recorded. The link below takes you to an article with a positive discussion about the benefits of recording consultations for doctors as well as 'patients', and you might wish to print it out and take it with you to consultations if you are planning to record them. See *aims.org.uk/rights* for a link to their information page. Most people are able to access a recording device that they can use when they are in a consultation or discussion with a midwife or doctor. Free recording device apps are available for both Android and Apple smartphones, and for those without a smartphone any other recording device will work just as well.

If you are in a consultation and don't have a recording device to hand, and the midwife or doctor says something that you are unsure about, you can ask them to write it down and sign it. For instance, if a doctor claims that your baby will be at risk if you don't accept a specific intervention, you can ask them to write this down and sign it (to confirm that they are happy that the information that they are sharing is accurate). If they are not confident that the information that they are giving is accurate, this should make them reflect on what they say.

Being clear and concise

Asking questions in a clear and concise way can help you to obtain the information that you need to be able to make your decisions. If you can, try to be clear and to the point when you are stating the decisions you have made and to communicate those decisions. Then you need to do all you can to ensure that those decisions are supported. Here are some examples:

- "What I need you to explain to me is…"
- "Please could you point me to the evidence about that?"
- "What is needed to make XYZ happen?"
- "I have decided that…" or "My decision is…"
- "That is not what was agreed. What I had agreed to is…"
- "I do not consent to…"
- "I need you to…"
- "I do consent to X, but I do not consent to Y."
- "I need time to make this decision."
- "How long would be reasonable for me to wait before I make this decision? Why?"
- "We have agreed that we will wait for another [insert time] before discussing this again, so please don't bring it up with me until then."
- "You need to stop that now."
- "Please don't touch me there."
- "No."

It might help to express how you feel about things:

- "I feel better when you…"
- "I am worried about…"
- "I feel scared about…"

- "I don't feel comfortable with…"
- "It would really help me if you could…"

There is no need to argue with midwives or doctors if you want to decline something. If you decide **not** to accept an offer of care, you don't need to persuade anyone of your decision. "Thank you, but no", or even just, "No" is enough. You don't need to sign any documents to confirm this if you don't want to.

However, if you are trying to negotiate access to care, for instance if you want to have a caesarean birth, it may help to gather evidence in support of your case. If a midwife or doctor agrees to a care option or package for something in the future, for instance agreeing access to a birth pool in hospital before labour starts, do ensure that they write down their agreement in your notes and sign it.

Repeating back

If you feel that what you are being told is either not accurate or is coercive, it might be helpful to repeat what you hear back to your midwife or doctor, ideally using the words that they used. This may help them to reflect on what they said. It can help to add your interpretation of what was said and perhaps, if you want to, how you feel about it. This can all help with the communication process.

For example, you might say, "So if I understand correctly, you are saying that I am not allowed to have a homebirth because I'm too old?"* You can then ask them to explain the details of their reasoning, and ask them to do so while you record these details, or ask them to write it down for you; this way they will be careful about offering accurate information, helping you to make an informed decision.

This isn't true – the only person who can legally decide whether to have a homebirth is the person giving birth.

Mirroring techniques

How people speak to us can sometimes reflect the way we speak to them! So, if you speak to a midwife or doctor in the way that you would like to be spoken to, it is more likely that they will speak to you in the same way. It's like a mirror. So it may help to be very polite and calm! (Be careful not to be too deferent because that can lead to some midwives and doctors feeling that they can or are supposed to make all the decisions.) If you expect to go straight into a fight (not an unreasonable feeling if you are trying to negotiate something) this itself can lead to a fight, so perhaps try to expect a positive negotiation instead! Imagine the scenario before you enter the room, and visualise two adults having a respectful conversation. Everyone appreciates being treated with kindness, and so this can make a difference in how you are treated in return. Kindness can lead to kindness.

This does not always work. Some midwives and doctors will treat people the same way no matter what. For many, how their own day is going will reflect the care that they give. Others will be able to put aside how they are feeling and focus solely on the person in front of them, no matter how awful their day is. That said, the *only* person who is responsible for how they treat women and people in their care is the midwife or doctor. It is *not* your responsibility if they are unkind, or if they are patronising, or coercive. If this happens, there are a number of options which I will cover below.

Leave the room

You can leave the room if you want to gather your thoughts, or you can ask the doctor or midwife to leave the room (for instance, if you are in labour and don't want to be the person who leaves!) You can stop a conversation at any time, if you want to. This is in your control. You can then ask to speak to someone else (which might be at a different time, depending on the circumstances) or choose to decline further care if you prefer. *You are in control.*

If you still haven't got enough information

If, after discussions with your midwife or doctor, you feel that you still do not have the information you need to make an informed decision, you can ask for a second opinion and/or do some research for yourself. You can also speak to someone more senior if you wish. Chapter 2 (p.13) details the different staff roles in the maternity services, so you can use this to help you to decide who else to contact.

Tools for decision making and asserting your rights

Using the BRAIN tool

You know that decisions are for you to make, not anyone else, and the BRAIN tool helps you to work through that decision-making process. BRAIN stands for:

» **Benefits**: How might this help, and what percentage of people would it be likely to help?

» **Repercussions (or Risks)**: What might be the downsides or unwanted consequences of this, and what percentage of people are likely to experience these consequences?

» **Alternatives**: Are there any alternatives to this intervention, test or treatment that I should consider? Sometimes there are multiple ways to deal with an issue.

» **Intuition**: What does my intuition, my gut feeling, tell me? Can I find time to sit with my thoughts and feelings, and see what I really feel, physically and/or emotionally about this? Is there anything my body can tell me that I need to listen to?

» **Nothing**: What would happen if I did nothing, and declined consent for this intervention, test or treatment? Could I have it later if I change my mind?

The BRAIN acronym is an excellent mental checklist that offers a reminder of questions that might be helpful to ask, as well as a reminder to check in with your own thoughts, feelings and intuition.

For more information on making decisions, see the AIMS Birth Information page 'Making decisions about your maternity care' – *aims.org. uk/rights*.

Be persistent (The Stuck Record!)

This technique is helpful if you have made a decision that you want something that you are not yet being given. It simply means to repeat what you have said, perhaps in different ways, and to be persistent. You shouldn't need to do this if you want to decline something as you don't need to persuade anyone of that – although in some situations, if you are being pressured into accepting something you don't want, you may need to be repetitive. For instance, repeatedly saying, "I have said no thank you, please stop asking me", perhaps escalating to, "I am now feeling that you are attempting to coerce me. What do I need to do to stop you doing this?" In some situations you might want to say, "Stop talking about this now."

This can be a helpful technique in a homebirth situation if the person that you are speaking to at the hospital is saying that "a midwife is not available". In this situation we recommend that someone other than the person giving birth does the negotiating (see Chapter 7 p.81).

Another example of where the stuck record technique may be valuable is if you feel that something is wrong and that you are not being listened to properly. For instance, if your instinct tells you that something is wrong with your baby, and you feel that they really do need to be born quickly but you are not being listened to, be persistent. Keep repeating yourself until you are heard.

It is often helpful to stay as calm as possible – or at the very least try to sound as calm as possible! Try to slow down your speech a little, take plenty of deep breaths, and take the time you need to formulate a calm response rather than react. If you are negotiating care while in the room with someone (as opposed to on the phone), try to be aware of your body language. If you are seated, place both your feet flat on the floor to ground yourself, and to show more assertive body language. If you are standing, stand with both feet firmly on the ground. Look the person that you are speaking to in the eye, if you feel you can. Visualise tension flowing away from your body and consciously try to relax. You may feel very anxious or distressed, but anything that you do to visualise and breathe tension away will have a positive effect, even if only a small one. Every small change can help.

Just as if you were on the phone, try to slow down your speech a little, and watch that your voice doesn't rise. Deliberately try to keep your voice sounding calm, even if you don't feel it inside. Supporting your body in this way can help you to stay calm and to come across as more confident than you feel.

Side-stepping barriers

In any negotiation it is helpful to know when it's time to move on because you are not getting the help you are looking for. Beating your head against a wall is debilitating, but sometimes you can find a way to side-step and walk around the wall. For example, if the person on the maternity ward switchboard won't put you through to the Head of Midwifery, consider whether you need to put the phone down and try the hospital's main phone line as a way to reach them. Or search online for their direct contact information, or perhaps ask local pregnant friends if they have their contact information. Think laterally and do not assume that because one person says 'no', that the answer is going to be the same from someone else.

Making a birth plan

It's true that you can't plan exactly how your birth will go and birth plans do not try to control the uncontrollable. However, birth plans do three very useful things:

- They help you to think about what your ideal birth would look like, and to plan for that situation, giving you the best chance of having the birth you want, whatever that looks like.
- They help you to think through, in advance of labour, what you feel you would or wouldn't want to happen in certain situations and to give you an opportunity to learn about what might happen so you're prepared for multiple eventualities.
- They help you to communicate this to anyone who is with you when you give birth so that they are aware of what is important to you.

Some people prefer to use the term 'birth preferences' rather than 'birth plan', but what you call your document is entirely up to you.

It is important to note that **a birth plan is not a document that means that you have given your consent to an intervention**. For instance, you might decide to write in your birth plan that you consent to a procedure, but if that procedure is offered to you, the midwife or doctor will need to ask for your consent again. Similarly, if you write in your birth plan that you consent to something but later change your mind, you are completely entitled to do this.

Sometimes, hospitals provide women with an outline birth plan, with tick boxes that appear to make decisions very simple. These can sometimes be helpful as part of a discussion about options and interventions, but they can also be overly simplistic. For instance, one question that was printed on one of these documents was, 'Would you like to have an injection after your baby is born to stop heavy bleeding?' and a yes/no option! The injection refers to the drug that is offered to help to release the placenta more quickly, and, like any drug, it has risks and benefits that are far more complicated than stated, so informed consent for this intervention cannot be given through this seemingly innocuous statement. If you have been offered this type of birth plan by your hospital you don't have to use it. However, you might find it helpful to have it as a starting point for things you want to think about.

It might be useful to plan for several scenarios, such as a homebirth, a hospital vaginal birth and a hospital caesarean birth so that if something unexpected happens in labour, and there are new decisions to make, you have already thought about what is important to you.

Sometimes, women and people find that during labour their birth plan is ignored, either partially or completely. This can be extremely distressing and sometimes traumatising and some people say this is a reason to not make a birth plan at all. However, there is no benefit in saying that a pregnant woman or person should not think about what is right for them, just in case it's ignored. Midwives and doctors should respect birth plans and empathically discuss any problems that may arise, including those that haven't been specifically considered in the birth plan, by supporting the person giving birth to make decisions. Where possible, it can be helpful to talk through your birth plan with your midwife and your birth supporters before labour, so everyone is familiar with it. If your birth supporters have a copy of it with them when you are in labour, they can refer to it whenever it is needed.

We do know that the risk of psychological trauma when things go wrong in birth is lowest when women and people are listened to, when they are given information so they can understand what is happening, and when they are supported in their decisions. If something happens that is not covered in the birth plan, good care means continuing to support the birthing woman or person by giving them impartial information about their options and supporting them with their decisions.

For more information on making decisions, see the AIMS Birth Information page, 'Making decisions about your maternity care' via *aims.org.uk/rights*.

Chapter 4

Healthcare providers and their obligations to you

Every doctor, every midwife, every healthcare provider involved in your care, whether you're having a really straightforward pregnancy or one with many complications, is obliged both by law and their own code of conduct to recognise that the only person who can make decisions about your body is you.

Right to be treated with dignity and respect

The NHS Constitution states, 'You have the right to be treated with dignity and respect, in accordance with your human rights.' See *aims.org.uk/rights*.

The Care Quality Commission (CQC) defines dignity and respect as:

> '...providers must make sure that they provide care and treatment in a way that ensures people's dignity and treats them with respect at all times. This includes making sure that people have privacy when they need and want it, treating them as equals and providing any support they might need to be autonomous, independent and involved in their local community. Providers must have due regard to the protected characteristics as defined in the Equality Act 2010.'

See the CQC Guidance on dignity and respect via *aims.org.uk/rights*.

The right for the pregnant woman or person to decide what happens to their body

When we are pregnant, the baby or babies we are carrying have no rights in law before they are born. This is because if a fœtus had rights, the only way to support those rights would be to impose interventions on the person who is pregnant, and that would be against their human rights. One person cannot be forced to undertake surgery, to take drugs or have any other test or intervention in order to potentially benefit another person. For instance, we cannot be forced to donate a kidney or even give blood, even if it is needed to save someone else's life. The same applies to pregnancy. A pregnant woman or person cannot be forced into a caesarean, induction, test or any other intervention, even if declining the intervention may cause harm to the foetus, because this would be against that woman or person's rights to decide what happens to their body.

Midwives, doctors, health visitors and other healthcare providers are not allowed by law or their code of conduct to threaten a pregnant woman or person as a way to obtain compliance. On the AIMS helpline we occasionally hear that someone has been threatened with a referral to Children's Services for not complying with a suggested treatment. Threatening a person with a referral to Children's Services if they do not agree to an intervention during pregnancy or birth would be illegal coercion, as the pregnant woman or person has the right to decide what happens to their body even if it might lead to harm, or even the death of, the unborn baby. Similarly, social workers are not allowed to coerce a pregnant woman or person into accepting an intervention in pregnancy or birth, or a birth decision such as location of birth, by threatening them with the removal of their baby if they don't comply.

Any agreement to an intervention as a consequence of being threatened may not be legal consent, so the midwife or doctor undertaking the intervention may not actually have received consent to do so.

Parental responsibility and consent to treatment of your baby

After birth, the baby is recognised as his or her own person with legal rights. The people with the rights to make medical decisions on behalf of the baby are the people with parental responsibility, which will usually be the woman or person who gave birth to the baby, and the other person on the birth certificate. However, there are situations where other people have parental rights, for instance after adoption. It is the people with parental responsibility, not the doctors or midwives, who have the right to decide what medical care to accept or decline on behalf of the baby.

There are strict legal rules that healthcare providers have to follow if they want to overrule the wishes of the people who have parental responsibility, which may include requesting support from Children's Services. However, it is only the courts that can override parental rights.

Threatening parents with a referral to Children's Services if they do not comply with medical care that is offered means that if the parents then give consent, it is not valid consent. Having said that, the situation in the UK's Family Law courts, which are held behind closed doors, is currently very worrying. AIMS is aware of cases where Children's Services have coerced women into interventions, or where women have been taken to court because their social worker feels that they have made decisions which may have put their unborn baby at risk, and the outcomes have not always been in favour of the mother despite the law being written in a way that means that she should have her body autonomy protected. If you are having problems with Children's Services, we urge you to seek early support. It is extremely important that you do not wait until things become serious. The Family Rights Group specialises in offering legal support to families who are in this situation, and Birthrights have useful information on their website. You can find their websites via *aims.org.uk/rights*.

There is more information about referrals to Children's Services later in this chapter (p.49) and in *The AIMS Guide to Resolution after Birth*. The AIMS helpline team can provide you with information and support – see *aims.org.uk/rights*.

Right to be provided with information

If a midwife or doctor is offering any form of test or intervention, they are obliged by law to offer to explain what it is, why they are offering it and the risks and benefits of it.

An important legal case, known as Montgomery v Lanarkshire (2015), clarified the law on what is required of a healthcare professional when they are discussing the risks and benefits of any aspect of medical care. Mrs Montgomery sued the Lanarkshire health board after her baby was injured during his birth, stating that she had not been given enough information to make an informed decision about her birth options. The court agreed, and the judgement explained that **patients have the right to be given all of the information that would be relevant and important to them as an individual.**

If you feel that you are not being given all of the information which is relevant to you, it may be helpful to mention this judgment as a reminder of your rights. The information should be given in an unbiased way, and you should not feel under pressure to accept any intervention or test.

Visit *aims.org.uk/rights* to read more information about the details of the Montgomery case, and how it affects health care.

The right not to have the information

The 'Montgomery' case can sometimes be misinterpreted by midwives and doctors to mean that they are also obliged to tell a pregnant woman or person about all the risks and benefits of *not* accepting an intervention, test, medication, etc. *This is not quite true.* They are obliged to offer to tell you, you are not obliged to listen.

While in many situations it will be helpful to listen to the information that the doctor or midwife wants to discuss, it is important for you to know that you have the right to *not* listen and that you can stop any conversation that is not working for you. For instance, if you feel that you are being coerced, rather than being part of a helpful information-sharing discussion, you can choose to step away from it even if you are told that they 'have to' say what they want to say to you. Similarly, if you have already made up your mind about declining something, and if you find that you keep being pressurised into discussing it "because we have to tell you all the risks", you know that you don't need to listen if you prefer not to.

You do not need to sign anything to say that you are declining an offer or a discussion of an offer of any medical treatment, but it should be documented in your notes.

> **You do not need to give someone permission (i.e. give consent) to *not* perform an intervention or test on you.**
> **Therefore, you can choose to *not* discuss the intervention or test if you want to.**

For example, a midwife may want to perform a stretch and sweep (see Chapter 8 p.108) at a routine antenatal appointment because their hospital guidelines state to offer it at your gestation.

Situation 1)

You may feel that you want more information about sweeps, in which case you can have the discussion about the benefits and risks with your midwife before making a decision about whether or not it's right for you. You don't have to make a decision there and then. If you're not sure, you can go away and think about it, talk to other people, get a second opinion, whatever helps you to feel that you have the information you need for your decision, and plan to see your midwife again if you decide to go ahead with one.

Situation 2)

You may have already decided to have a sweep, but your midwife is still obliged to discuss the benefits and risks with you before doing it to ensure that s/he is clear that you are making an informed decision, and she is performing the intervention with your fully informed consent. Although this may not happen in practice, it is a legal requirement.

Situation 3)

You may have already decided not to have a sweep, in which case the midwife is obliged to *offer* to explain the benefits and risks but you can simply say, "Thank you, but I have decided that I do not want to have a sweep, and I don't wish to discuss it".

Summary

1. If you are certain that you *don't* want the intervention, treatment or test, you are not obliged to have a discussion about it.

2. If you *do* want the intervention or test, the midwife or doctor who does it needs to know, for their own protection, that you have made an informed decision. That information will normally be given in a conversation between you and them, but could be obtained in another way, for instance by giving you a leaflet. They are obliged to ensure that the information is given to you in a form that you can understand so, for example, if the leaflet is not in a language that you speak, this would not be sufficient. You are entitled to ask for more information if you don't feel that you have been told everything, or if you want to discuss things further.

3. If you are not sure whether you want it or not, you have the right to have as much or as little information about it as you need in order to make a decision. If you choose to have it, then the midwife or doctor does need to ensure that you have been given enough information to make an informed decision.

Consequences of tests

Some interventions and tests appear to be benign, but the results may have important consequences. This needs to be part of the discussion that your midwife or doctor has with you before you decide whether or not to have the test or intervention. For instance, if you are being tested for gestational diabetes, simply taking the test may not seem to be a big deal. What really matters, though, is what the result is. You might find it helpful to know if it's positive, because you would be happy to make any recommended changes to your diet and exercise regime, or, possibly, to take the medications that some women with gestational diabetes are recommended. However, a positive result may also mean that you are strongly pushed into a care plan that you don't want, that some birth options become harder to access, and that you are offered more scans and monitoring, which themselves may have risks and benefits you need to consider. You should have all of this explained to you in advance of the test so that you can decide whether or not you want to accept the offer. (Readers who wish to learn more about gestational diabetes will find the AIMS book *Gestational Diabetes* helpful. You can buy the book in print or Kindle format via the AIMS website: *aims.org.uk/rights*.)

However, this rarely happens. The main reason is a lack of time; midwives and doctors, like most healthcare providers, are bound by unworkable time constraints and they often don't have enough time to go through the issues thoroughly with the woman or person in front of them. You don't have to accept being rushed into a decision because your midwife or doctor is busy or in a hurry. It is important to know that you have the right to take the time you need to make a decision. This may mean that you need to make another appointment, if the decision can wait. If it can't wait, you can simply explain that you haven't had enough information and/or time, and that you need more time with the midwife or doctor before you can make your decision. This can put stress on the midwives and doctors, and we can all empathise with that. However, it is not the pregnant woman or person's responsibility to manage the health service's staffing levels. Our bodies, our pregnancies and our births are our personal responsibility, and as such if you need more time to make a decision, or if you need to obtain more information, you have the right to have it. Remember, some of these decisions could affect you or your baby or babies for the rest of your lives, and you matter! Ensuring that we have the time and information to make our decisions is ensuring that we respect and support ourselves and our own worth.

Another reason why pregnant women and people may not be given the full list of risks and benefits is fear of the consequences for the staff if they don't follow their hospital's guidelines. Midwives and doctors can find that they face repercussions from their managers or colleagues if they do not persuade a woman or person to accept the intervention that the relevant guideline suggests. If there is an adverse outcome for either the mother/birthing parent or baby, the midwife or doctor will almost always have to justify why they didn't follow the hospital's guidelines. If an intervention that was in the hospital's guidelines *is* done, they are less likely to have to justify this, even when the intervention itself caused problems to mother/birthing parent or baby.

Generally speaking, it's far easier for the midwife or doctor if a woman accepts the tests and interventions which are recommended in the hospital's guidelines, even if these are not what the woman or person wants. This can sometimes lead to a lot of pressure and coercion from the midwife or doctor, with the benefits of the intervention being overstated, and the risks being downplayed or ignored.

Again, while we can empathise with the challenges that midwives and doctors face, it is totally reasonable to prioritise our own bodies and babies. We are the experts in our own bodies and personal lives and are best placed to make our decisions based on what is right for us. Remember that guidelines, no matter who has published them, are not rules, laws or protocols, and we do not have to follow them. There is more detail about guidelines in Chapter 7 (p.81).

Under pressure to consent?

Once you have made a decision to decline a test or intervention, your decision should be respected. You should not be put under pressure to discuss it further. If you decide it would be helpful to discuss it further with someone else that is fine, but you are not obliged to attend any further appointments to discuss a particular course of action or inaction unless you want to. If you do want to listen, you should be given impartial and evidence-based information, without any cherry picking of the evidence, and, where the evidence is of poor quality, or missing, or where it's based on opinion rather than evidence, that should be explained.

If a woman or person is coerced into giving their agreement, then the law is very clear that this is not consent. So for example, if a doctor uses a phrase like "we don't want a dead baby/we're just doing the best thing for baby" to scare a woman or person into agreeing to a particular pathway or intervention, this is coercion and not valid consent. To use an example in another area of criminal law, if a woman has sex with a man because he tells her that if she doesn't, he will harm her in another way, she has been coerced, and has not given consent in law. She has still been raped, even if she apparently agreed to sex. While this may seem like an extreme example, it is a really important one because we clearly understand that, in that situation, consent has not been given, even if the woman says, "yes".

Emmeline May from Rockstardinosaurpirateprincess.com created an extremely helpful animation on the meaning of consent, called 'Tea and Consent'. It uses the analogy of offering someone a cup of tea and supporting their decision whether they accept or decline the offer – or change their mind halfway through. Do watch it – it's excellent! See 'Consent and tea – a video' at *aims.org.uk/rights*.

Exactly the same law applies if a midwife or doctor obtains agreement by making the person feel they have no safe alternative, or threatens someone if they don't consent (for instance, with a threat of a referral to Children's Services). Any intervention that then takes place under such duress is done without valid consent and is therefore not done with informed consent, and may therefore be criminal assault and battery.

I have used the example of a woman or person being told that if they do not comply their baby might die because it is a threat that is not uncommon, and it's one of the worst things that, as parents, we can hear, so it's a very powerful threat. Of course, there will be occasions when there are serious concerns for a baby, but if a baby is genuinely at risk, this should be calmly and sensitively explained. It is essential, therefore, that every person who accesses the maternity services knows that they are entitled to have the time to really understand the situation, and that they are entitled to accurate and evidence-based information provided in a sensitive and supportive manner.

Other examples of coercion

Example 1

A person is not permitted to have pain relief until they agree to a vaginal examination.

In this example, the vaginal exam would be done under coercion, which is not 'informed consent'. Some forms of pain relief may be better given earlier in labour (e.g. pethidine) – or later (e.g. epidural). However, vaginal exams are not a good way to judge how far through labour a person is and, while there are other ways to 'guesstimate' it, it can never be judged completely accurately every time. A birthing woman or person is entitled to the information on the benefits and risks of the pain relief requested or offered, and on how those benefits and risks are affected by how far into labour a person is. They are then entitled to make a decision based on this information.

You have the same legal right to put your fingers in the vagina or body orifice of your midwife or doctor as they do to put theirs in yours – that is, none whatsoever, unless the person consents to it happening. Your vagina, your rules. The same applies to any medical treatment, test, medication or intervention. Your body, your rules.

Read more about vaginal examinations in labour at the AIMS website: *aims.org.uk/rights*. You might also find the AIMS information page, 'Ways of managing your labour' to be helpful, also at *aims.org.uk*.

Example 2

A woman is told that a specific medical condition means that she 'has to' birth in hospital with continuous monitoring and a cannula because she's likely to bleed heavily after birth.

It may be that the individual woman in this example has a higher chance of heavy bleeding after birth compared to another woman or person. A personalised discussion means that the woman can decide for herself whether any risks are likely to happen, and whether they are serious enough to consider an intervention to reduce that risk. It is also important to look at the risks of each intervention. **What is important here is the phrase "she has to". She doesn't have to do anything.**

There is no doubt that it can be very difficult for some people not to feel that they are 'being a nuisance' or 'challenging the doctors or midwives'. But this isn't a challenge and you don't need to fight. Ultimately, it's your body and your baby that is going to be affected by your decisions. Midwives and obstetricians may have far more knowledge about pregnancy and birth than most people, but they don't know everything. Most importantly, they don't have the knowledge that you, and only you, as the person who is creating a new baby or babies, has about your own body. You are the person best placed to decide what's right for you. **You are the expert in you.**

How to recognise if you are being coerced

It doesn't matter if the coercion is happening with 'the best intentions', nor whether the midwife or doctor is really nice and friendly. Their obligation is to give impartial information and not to try to force you one way or another. Whether they are trying to encourage a woman or person towards or away from an intervention (rather than providing them with the information and supporting them with their decision) they are at risk of breaking the law.

If any of the following are happening:

- you are being told what is going to happen / what is going to be done to you,
- you are told that you have to have a vaginal exam before you are 'allowed' something,
- you are expected to do something that does not feel right for you,
- you do not have enough information to be able to make a decision,
- you are being asked to justify your decision to decline something,
- you are being put under pressure, bullied, threatened or forced,

then you might be being coerced.

Coercion isn't necessarily something that the midwife or doctor is doing deliberately or consciously, and it's rare that it's done with intentional unkindness. Midwives and doctors are often unaware that they are coercing you as it's normal for them to tell pregnant women and people what will happen rather than to have a discussion where the pregnant person is expected to decide. But, no matter the intention, coercion is taking away from your power to decide for yourself and, therefore, it is not ok. Trust your instinct.

What you can do if you feel that you are being coerced

Remember that it is you who makes the decisions. First, in almost all but the most extreme emergency situations you have the time to think about things or talk things through and get more information. Even in emergencies you will usually have a few minutes to think and decide. In most cases you will be able to say things like:

- "I've not yet decided whether I want to do that. Could you talk me through the risks and benefits again please?"
- "Does this need to be done immediately or have we got time to discuss it?"
- "That's helpful, thank you, I will go away and think about it and let you know my decision at my next appointment."
- "I'm not sure that this feels right for me. Who else can I talk to about this?"
- "I have thought about this and have decided that this is not right for me."

For some situations, the doctor or midwife might need to be reminded of their obligations under their code of practice. The Nursing and Midwifery Council (NMC), which regulates nurses and midwives, states that midwives must 'respect, support and document a person's right to accept or refuse care and treatment'. See *aims.org.uk/rights*.

The doctor's regulator, the General Medical Council (GMC), states,

'The patient weighs up the potential benefits, risks and burdens of the various options as well as any non-clinical issues that are relevant to them. The patient decides whether to accept any of the options and, if so, which one. They also have the right to accept or refuse an option for a reason that may seem irrational to the doctor, or for no reason at all.' See *aims.org.uk/rights*.

If you find yourself in a situation where you are really struggling to get a midwife or doctor to stop trying to persuade you into something that you know you don't want, pointing out these parts of the code will normally make them recognise that they need to stop talking.

Threat of a referral to Children's Services

As outlined in Chapter 1 (p.7), consent to treatment must be given freely for it to be legal. If consent is given because of a threat, it is not given freely and therefore not legal and any healthcare provider who undertakes an intervention on that woman or person may be accused of assault and battery.

The role of Children's Services (sometimes known as Social Services) is explained in Chapter 2 (p.13). Midwives, doctors and other healthcare providers may threaten a pregnant woman or person with a referral to Children's Services if they do not agree to a particular care pathway, and sometimes Children's Services will threaten a pregnant woman or person with consequences, including the removal of their child after birth if they do not comply with medical advice. As you know, this is illegal coercion.

Unfortunately, the laws protecting the body autonomy of pregnant women and people are not always upheld by medical staff, Children's Services or even the family courts. For this reason, it is imperative that if you start to experience threats of this kind that you seek immediate support (see below). In addition, AIMS recommends that you ask for the threats to be put in writing, or that you record them (remember, you have the right to record a consultation but in this case you may need to ask the person to repeat what they said for the recording).

For support on these issues, we recommend that you contact either the Family Rights Group, Birthrights or a lawyer who specialises in this area. See *aims.org.uk/rights* for contact information.

Some practical ways to deal with coercion

If you are being coerced into agreeing to something against your will, it can be helpful to use similar techniques to those you would use to obtain information (see also Chapter 3 p.24). The aim is to get the midwife and/or doctor to think carefully about what they are saying and how they are saying it and whether they would want it on record, were it to be challenged.

Record the conversation (there are free recording apps for smartphones on the App Store/ Play Store). When a person knows they are being recorded, they are more likely to be cautious about what they say.

Ask the midwife or doctor to write down what they are saying. Putting their words in writing means that they are often more careful to be non-coercive. Use phrases like, "Please could you go through with me why you are offering this intervention?" Using words like 'offer' reminds the midwife or doctor that they must offer something, not tell you what will happen.

If you have declined an offer of care, you might like to reassure your midwife or doctor that you will seek medical care if something changes that you are concerned about. If you are being harassed about your decision, you can also simply decide that you do not want to continue with a conversation and explain that you will have to leave if they don't stop coercing you. You have the power to decide whether or not to remain in a room with someone who is not communicating with you in an appropriate way, and the power to ask someone to leave the room if you are labouring, having treatment or if you are in your own home.

When thinking about what you want, you might find it helpful to write down what you have decided, or write down questions if you want to know more. Taking a supportive friend, partner, doula or someone else you trust might be helpful. Remember, you don't need to justify to a midwife or doctor why you don't want to accept their offer of an intervention, nor do you need to persuade them of your point of view. You can simply say, "no thank you" and decline to discuss it further. You do not have to explain or convince them about why your decision is the right one for you and they do not have a right to an explanation. You are equally entitled to have that discussion if you wish. It's your choice.

Having said that, if you are requesting something (rather than declining it), such as a caesarean or a specific pain relief option, having it clear in your mind (and maybe on paper) why this is important to you might be helpful, and have to hand any research to hand which backs up your position.

Changing your midwife, doctor or other healthcare provider

You are not obliged to continue to see any midwife, doctor or other healthcare provider such as a health visitor if you don't want to. You can ask to be allocated someone different for any reason (and you don't have to give the reason) and you can also decide that you don't want to see any of them. This is the case whether you are pregnant, in labour or after birth. There are some limits to this. For instance, if you want to have a female obstetrician and there are only male obstetricians in the hospital while you are in labour, it may not be possible for a female doctor to attend you, although if you agree to see a male doctor a chaperone must be made available for you if you want one. You are still at liberty to decline care from the available doctors if you wish to.

Your risk status

» Risk factors can mean that we are told that we **should** have an intervention **and**
» Risk factors can mean that we are told that we **cannot** access a service.

In the UK, every pregnant woman is allocated a binary risk status – high or low. Being 'high risk' tends to mean that women are told that they may not access certain services, for instance a birth centre, or that they might need an intervention, such as continuous monitoring.

And yet we are all individuals with differing needs, wishes and concerns. We are not simply one thing or another. An individual overweight woman might easily be fitter and healthier than a woman of a perceived healthy weight, but the heavier woman is more likely to be labelled as 'high risk' solely based on her weight.

There is also no detail within the high risk label. A woman who has previously experienced excessive blood loss after birth (often called post-partum haemorrhage, or PPH) is likely to be classed as high risk, but her needs are totally different to a woman with diabetes, or a person carrying triplets, or a woman who broke her pelvis twenty years ago – yet the high risk label is applied to them all – and each might be told that their birth options are limited in similar ways, even though they have completely different medical needs.

Pregnant women and people should be given the opportunity to have a personalised discussion about any risk factors that apply to them and their significance, if any, to them personally. This might be with a specialist midwife for diabetes, or an obstetrician, and this support can be crucial in obtaining information and accessing specialist care if required.

However, many pregnant women and people find that because they have been labelled as high risk they are expected to have a more medicalised pregnancy and birth than they want, or are denied access to services such as birth centres or waterbirth.

Therefore, during these conversations, the first thing that you need to know is *what* adverse outcome(s) you are thought to be at higher risk *of* – that is, to find out the detail of the risk factor(s) that you are thought to have. You then need to know:

- What the chances are of this outcome happening compared to women who don't have this risk factor? (See box below.)
- Once you know this you can find out what they can offer to reduce

the chance of this outcome, and you can decide whether or not you want to accept that offer.

- If you are told that you cannot access a service (eg a Midwifery Led Unit, or birth pool) you can find out exactly why the risk factor means that you are being told this, and work out whether this really applies to you.

Don't hesitate to take along any information you may have gathered elsewhere to discuss its relevance to you and ask for the midwife or doctor's thoughts on it, if you want to. Chapter 3 (p.24) has suggestions on how to encourage midwives and doctors to give you the information you need to make an informed decision rather than trying to encourage you down their preferred pathway.

It is important to understand how risks can be presented. For instance, if the chance of an adverse outcome is 1 in 1,000 people, and a risk factor means that this increases to 2 in 1,000 people, this can be presented as being "double the risk", which sounds really worrying. However, if you are given the actual numbers, it is clear that the risk is very low.

For more information about understanding risk, please visit the AIMS Birth Information page, 'Understanding quantitative research evidence' at *aims.org.uk/rights*.

If you are told that you cannot access a service due to your risk factor(s), you can ask for a written, complete explanation of the reasons why, including the details of any research evidence. This can help you to address the concerns one by one, and gives you something concrete to negotiate with.

Once you feel that you have had enough time and information to make your decision, and you understand the risks and benefits of all your options, including that of any intervention(s), you may well decide that certain interventions feel right for you, or you may decide to decline some or all of them. The AIMS Birth Information page, 'Making decisions about your maternity care' may be helpful here – see *aims.org.uk/rights*.

Example situation

A woman who has previously had an unusually heavy bleed after a previous birth (post partum haemorrhage, or PPH) might be told that she 'has to' give birth on the obstetric unit and that she isn't 'allowed' a homebirth (of course, by now you know that only you do the allowing). She may be advised that she has to have continuous monitoring (because she's high risk) and that she 'must' have the injection to assist with the birth of her placenta. As she's high risk she may be told that she is not 'allowed' to use the pool – but that she can have an epidural.

In fact, the decision about where she gives birth is hers, and if she doesn't want to birth in the obstetric unit, she doesn't need to. She is free to accept all of these suggestions, but she may prefer to look at the benefits and risks of each of these interventions.

She might start by finding out why she had a PPH after her previous birth. Her notes are available free in the UK by writing to the hospital under which she gave birth, or from her independent midwife if she had one (see the section 'Right to access your notes' on page 56). Perhaps the PPH was caused by a severe tear, which would only be an issue if she had another tear, or perhaps it was because someone pulled on her baby's umbilical cord in a way that caused a bleed. She may recall feeling scared, uncomfortable or unsupported or perhaps her baby was taken away for a while. The levels of an important labour hormone, oxytocin, which is responsible for uterine contractions (as well as other things) is raised by feeling safe, secure and cared for, and also by skin to skin with our babies, and breast suckling. When oxytocin levels drop, the uterus doesn't always contract effectively and this can cause a PPH. Therefore, looking at these environmental factors is also important.

The reason why the PPH happened is important in judging whether there's a higher chance of it happening again. It might be that there would not be any benefit from being continuously monitored, nor that the pool would be a problem at all – in fact water may keep the woman feeling more secure, warm and comfortable, therefore increasing her oxytocin levels. Birthing at home has been shown to lower the risk of PPH (see *aims.org.uk/rights*) and therefore this may benefit her. Individualised care means looking at all of these factors and not just being denied certain options, or carrying out more interventions which may not be helpful because of a high risk label.

For many years, AIMS has campaigned for Continuity of Carer, meaning that all pregnant women and people would have a midwife that they know and trust who can care for them through pregnancy, birth and during the postnatal period. There is strong evidence of better outcomes for mothers and babies, including a reduction in the rate of stillbirth, but despite several Government proposals to bring Continuity of Carer to midwifery, at the time of writing most pregnant women and people are not being provided with this type of care. Having a known and trusted midwife means that these conversations about 'risk factors' happen in the context of a relationship where the midwife knows the mother really well, and is therefore far better placed to provide very personalised care. You can ask your hospital whether they have a Continuity of Carer service, as some will for some people, and, if not, ask them to offer it to you anyway. The more women and people who show that this is important to them, the more chance there is of this important service being implemented. For more information about Continuity of Carer, see the following Chapter 5.

Making a complaint

If you wish to make a complaint to or about the provider of your maternity services, we recommend reading the AIMS book, *The AIMS Guide to Resolution After Birth*. The book offers comprehensive and empathic information about how to reach a resolution after a distressing maternity experience. It takes the reader through the emotional side of seeking resolution, which can be very mentally and physically challenging, and also provides information on the different pathways for making a complaint. There is comprehensive nformation on the many organisations that can help. You can read more about the book, which is available in printed or Kindle format, on the AIMS website – *aims.org.uk/rights*.

Right to access your notes

It is a good idea to obtain a copy of your health records, sometimes referred to as case notes as well as your maternity hand held notes if you have had to return those, before making a complant. You have the right to see and receive a copy of all your health records and those of your baby – the records will include written notes, any computerised records and any additional letters or memos.

Although it isn't permitted for the hospital to delete anything from the notes (they can add to them), it has sometimes happened. Sometimes, important parts of the notes can be 'lost' if a complaint is made about a specific part of the birth. Having your own copy ensures that they cannot be tampered with after the fact, or, if they are, you have evidence of this.

Under GDPR, the law which covers your rights over your personal information and how it is used, you can obtain a copy of your notes without any charge. To do this, find out how to contact your local Patient Advice and Liaison Service (PALS) which should be on your hospital's website, and send them a request with your name, address, date of birth and the date of birth of your baby. You have the right to obtain your baby's notes free of charge as well.

Chapter 5

Antenatal care

You're pregnant! Congratulations! So what now? This chapter aims to help you to understand the different options for pregnancy care and for planning for your birth. The decisions, of course, are all yours.

Confirming your pregnancy

Most people confirm their pregnancy using a home test kit, although some people know they are pregnant and don't feel the need for a test. A positive test, even if the line is really faint, means that you are almost certainly pregnant and there's no need to buy an expensive version to confirm it, unless you want to. This is because the test looks for a pregnancy hormone called human chorionic gonadotrophin (HCG) which is only in the body when we're pregnant, or for a short while after pregnancy, so it's rare to have a false positive. However, sometimes a pregnancy may begin but end in a very early miscarriage. In this case, a test may show as positive for a while after the miscarriage as there are still pregnancy hormones in the body. Other reasons for a false positive include some drugs, some fertility drugs, and an ectopic pregnancy. For more information on ectopic pregnancy, see the AIMS website – *aims.org.uk.*

A negative test may mean you're not pregnant, or it might mean that you are but that there is not yet enough HCG in the body for the test to detect it, so it is worth testing again in a few days. Ideally it is best to wait until you are past the time when your period is due when there will usually be enough HCG for most tests to be able to detect it.

You have the right to obtain a free pregnancy test at some NHS sexual health clinics, some Brook Centres, and some GPs. Visit the NHS website for more information on pregnancy tests via *aims.org.uk/rights.*

Early pregnancy scans

You may want to have an early pregnancy scan, which is possible from about 7 weeks, and sometimes an early scan is recommended by their doctor. There are many reasons why you might want to have an early scan, or why you might be offered one, including:

- if you are in pain or have some bleeding
- if you have a history of miscarriage and want reassurance about the pregnancy
- if you've had fertility treatment and are looking for additional confirmation of pregnancy
- to check for a possible ectopic pregnancy.

These early scans can be hugely important to pregnant women or people who want the reassurance that at this stage the pregnancy is developing as hoped, although scans cannot guarantee that the pregnancy will continue.

You don't have the right to have an early pregnancy scan on the NHS without a medical reason, but if you are showing signs of a serious medical situation such as an ectopic pregnancy, this should be provided as a matter of urgency. For those having fertility treatment it may be planned as part of your care. Private scanning clinics may be able to offer an early scan, but you will need to pay and you might want to check that the person doing the scan is a qualified sonographer (holds a qualification in Medical or Clinical Ultrasound) as there is no requirement for this to be the case.

Scans done through the abdomen before about 11 weeks may not be clear enough, so you may be offered a trans-vaginal scan. You might also be offered this type of scan after about 11 or 12 weeks if the pregnancy isn't showing well enough through an abdominal scan. This procedure involves a probe being inserted into your vagina which, while tolerable for many, can be very uncomfortable for some people, and some can find it very distressing. If you do not wish to have this you can say no. However, if you decline it you may not be able to get the information you want solely from an abdominal scan.

If you are offered an early pregnancy scan but don't want one, you have the right to decline it.

Booking with a midwife

Booking with an NHS midwife and questions they may ask

Everyone who is pregnant and who has the right to NHS care has the right to a midwife through the NHS. Most pregnant women and people are able to book with an NHS midwife by contacting their own GP surgery, as most have a midwifery service attached to the surgery. If your area has a different system, the GP surgery will explain this. You may be able to book directly with an NHS midwife, and some areas have community hubs that you can approach without going via the GP surgery.

Booking with an NHS midwife is optional, although you will need to book if you wish to access routine NHS care.

Your pregnancy history

'Booking' involves a meeting with the midwife where they will ask you about your history of pregnancy and birth, if any, and any other related medical conditions including those of the genetic family of the baby, usually the father or sperm donor and baby's grandparents, where known. You do not have to share information that you don't want to share.

Possible tests

You do not have to be weighed, nor do you have to accept any of the tests that you'll be offered, even if you are told that "you have to". The decision is yours alone. The midwife should explain why the different tests are being offered and take the time to answer any questions you have until you are satisfied that you have enough information to make an informed decision, and the midwife must respect your decision.

Where do you want to give birth?

A question that you may be asked at booking is where you plan to have your baby, and you should be told about the options, which include at home, at a midwife-led unit or in hospital. You do not need to decide at this point, but if you want to you can state your plans. You can always change them later if you wish. In fact, some women and people decide to book a homebirth or midwife-led unit (MLU) birth anyway because they can still go the hospital when it comes to labour if they want to, so they're keeping their options open. It may be more complicated to access the MLU or have a midwife attend a homebirth if it hasn't been planned beforehand. Having said that, you can tell your midwife that you would like to have a homebirth or MLU birth at any time in your pregnancy.

Continuity of Carer

Continuity of Carer (mentioned near the end of Chapter 4), means having a known and trusted midwife throughout pregnancy, birth and the early postnatal period and has important safety benefits for both women/people and babies. For further information from each of the four countries in the UK, see *aims. org.uk/rights*.

NHS England published its 'Better Births' strategy in December 2017, where it was noted that:

'This continuity of care and relationship between caregiver and receiver has been proven to lead to better outcomes and safety for the woman and baby, as well as offering a more positive and personal experience; and was the single biggest request of women of their services that was heard during the Review.

The report went on to ask that all areas of England would, by October 2017, 'establish a shared vision and plan to implement Better Births by the end of 2020/21'. These plans are expected to show how most women will receive continuity of the person caring for them during pregnancy, birth and postnatally.

Unfortunately, there is still no absolute right to this within the NHS.

In Scotland, the '5-year Forward Plan' makes recommendations such as:
- All women will have continuity of midwifery carer from a primary midwife.
- Midwifery and obstetric teams will be aligned with a caseload of women and be co-located for the provision of community and hospital-based services.

In Wales, the 'Five year vision for the future' states that:
- All women will receive continuity of carer across their maternity journey with seamless links to specialist care when required.

- All women will have a named midwife; some may also need a named obstetrician who is responsible for planning care in partnership with the woman and her family.
- All women will receive antenatal and postnatal continuity of carer by no more than two midwives and two obstetric teams.

In Northern Ireland, 'A Strategy for Maternity Care in Northern Ireland 2012-2018' commits to, 'Continuity of Care for women throughout the maternity pathway.'

In 2020, in the document 'Midwifery 2020 – Delivering Expectations', all four countries of the UK committed to continuing to implement Continuity of Carer. See more at *aims.org.uk/rights*. If you are not being offered Continuity of Carer you may want to ask about who in your area is currently being provided with this type of care, and whether it is possible for you to access it as well.

At the time of writing there is little evidence of significant progress across much of the UK, and places where it is being provided are focused on certain groups of pregnant women or people, such as those planning a caesarean birth, or teenagers, or people who are considered to be especially vulnerable. In other areas, it is those who book homebirths who have access to Continuity of Carer. In most cases, however, the continuity comes from a team of midwives rather than one or two, so it may still not be possible to build up a close relationship with the person who attends your birth.

Ask your midwife what your local hospital offers, and do feel free to feed your wishes and needs back to them as strongly as you want to. The AIMS helpline will be able to support you if you wish – *aims.org.uk/rights*.

Booking with an independent midwife

At the time of writing (Autumn 2020), most independent midwives in the UK have been stopped from being able to attend births for the time being, but they can still offer the full range of antenatal and postnatal support. It is hoped that this issue will be resolved very soon, but if you are interested in hiring an independent midwife, they will talk to you about what they are able to do before agreeing a contract with you.

An independent midwife (IM) has the same training as a midwife working in the NHS and is registered with the NMC in the same way. They have to hold suitable liability insurance which they will explain to you. An independent midwife is not employed by the NHS, although she or he may also work for the NHS outside of your contract with them. There can be many reasons for booking with an IM including being sure to have a known and trusted midwife throughout pregnancy and the birth journey.

Some UK independent midwives work only in their local areas and others will travel. You can find them through word of mouth, social media, online, and some (but not all) are registered with the organisation Independent Midwives UK (IMUK). Some independent midwives work in small teams, so you may be offered care from several of them, but you can request that you are only seen by one, if you wish. Visit IMUK's website via *aims.org.uk/rights*.

Independent midwives normally provide all or most of your midwifery antenatal care, attend your birth and most offer extensive postnatal support. Care which involves equipment that the midwife won't have, such as a scan, can be done by the NHS (which will still be free for you if you are entitled to NHS care) or a private company.

Most independent midwives support homebirths, but if you decide to plan a hospital birth, you can still do all of your antenatal and postnatal sessions with them, usually in your own home, and they may be able to accompany you to hospital. However, they are unlikely to be able to act as your midwife in hospital if the hospital's liability guidelines don't normally allow this. It may be possible to negotiate this, but it would need to be done in advance because it would probably involve your midwife being provided with a contract to provide care.

If you are eligible for NHS services, booking an independent midwife does not change your right to access the NHS. You can 'dip in and out' of any part of the NHS service you choose, such as getting scans or other tests, and you can decide to give birth in hospital if you wish, or transfer to hospital in labour even if it's not what you planned. It's therefore important to consider whether you want to book with the NHS in the normal way, as well as with your independent midwife, so that they have you registered as a pregnant woman or person with the right to use the service should you need it. You don't need to interact with them in any way if you don't want to. However, even if you haven't booked with the NHS at the beginning of your pregnancy, you can choose to do so at later date.

Booking with a private company

Private homebirth companies offer a service which normally includes Continuity of Carer, similar to an independent midwife. However, their insurance policy may limit what they can offer, which might mean that if your circumstances change they are suddenly unable to care for you (including, for some situations, during labour), so check carefully what they are able to offer you. There are a small number of private hospitals in the UK. These may offer a more luxurious birthing experience than some NHS hospitals, although they tend to have higher rates of caesarean births than NHS hospitals, even for women who had planned a vaginal birth. Private hospitals usually don't have critical care facilities, so if you or your baby or babies become very unwell, you and/or they will be transferred to an NHS hospital.

Choosing antenatal classes

NHS birth preparation classes

NHS Trusts should offer pregnant women and people free classes to help them to prepare for birth and beyond. Although this is an important part of health care, these services have been cut back over the past few years, and in some Trusts they are only offering midwife-led classes to those people who they consider to be the most vulnerable. For the rest, an app or online videos are offered, which are unlikely to give enough information to prepare sufficiently for birth and beyond and do not allow for discussion or questions.

It is AIMS opinion that good birth preparation is one of the best ways for women and people to influence their chance of experiencing a positive, empowering and safe birth, and the happiest start to motherhood and parenthood, and therefore these cuts are unacceptable. If you wish to know more about planning your birth, but you are not offered access to an antenatal class, or you did not feel sufficiently prepared by the NHS antenatal services, you can ask for more time with your midwife to do this planning if you wish to.

Private providers of antenatal classes

There are a number of organisations which offer private, paid for antenatal classes. If you are on a low income, do ask whether they have any concessions as many offer discounts based on ability to pay.

You can find what classes are local to you by searching online, speaking to other parents-to-be or on social media. Sometimes they advertise in local newsletters or parenting magazines. Different types of classes may offer different types of birth preparation so it's worth shopping around to see what feels right for you, and talking to people about their experiences of classes. Some types of birth preparation, such as hypnobirthing, focus strongly on managing labour and understanding how to best work with our bodies, and many women find these tools to be powerful and effective (although of course nothing works for everyone). Other classes have a wider remit and include newborn baby care, so some people decide to do more than one type of course.

Group classes can be a wonderful way to meet other parents-to-be who are going through the same life changes as you and this may lead to life-long friendships. For others, private sessions are preferable. There's no right or wrong way.

A birth doula or independent midwife should be able to help you to decide what kind of birth is right for you, and work with you to prepare for that, as well as preparing for life with a baby. They may also have information about what other options for birth preparation are available locally.

Summary

Finding the right support during pregnancy can make all the difference to your experience of pregnancy, birth and becoming a parent. There are many options so it's really worth looking around and talking to different people before deciding what is right for you. You can decide to do no planning if you wish, or you can prepare with multiple different people or organisations. The decision is yours.

Chapter 6

Antenatal screening and tests

The pros and cons of having tests

As I have already mentioned, and no doubt will mention many more times, all tests and checks are optional. This is true for your entire pregnancy, your birth and beyond. You cannot, by law, be forced to accept *any* intervention or test, provided you have 'capacity', (see Chapter 1 p.7). This is because no one can touch our bodies, or do anything to them, unless we agree to it, and this does not change just because we are pregnant.

From the first visit to your midwife (if you choose to have one) you will be offered myriad tests. It is important to understand that each test may lead to consequences that might be of benefit and/or be detrimental to you. For instance, a beneficial outcome may be that the test picks up a medical condition that would be better if it were treated. A detrimental outcome may be that you are told that you 'have to' do something, such as have antibiotics in labour if you are shown to have Group B Strep, or that you 'can't' do something else, such as birth in water if your BMI is considered to be 'too high' (of course you now know you don't 'have to'). In some instances, tests may undermine trust between a pregnant woman or person, and midwife.

Example of pros and cons:

* Finding out that you have high blood pressure is beneficial because it can, if necessary, be treated. However, it might mean that you are told that you "have to" birth in the obstetric unit, rather than in a midwife-led unit (MLU) or at home. You have the right to birth at home, and you may be able to negotiate access to the midwife-led unit, but it is likely to be less straightforward than if you don't have high blood pressure. There is also the risk of a 'false positive', which means that the result of the test was wrong. Or perhaps you might have 'white coat syndrome' which means that your blood pressure is fine, but it becomes high when you are around medical staff. This might lead you to be diagnosed with high blood pressure, and even be treated for it, when you don't actually need the treatment.

* Monitoring for carbon monoxide (CO) is offered to most pregnant women and people. The test is to see whether the woman or person is a smoker, and, if so, to be offered stop smoking services. The test may also detect someone who is affected by second hand (passive) smoking but who may not realise that it's affecting their body and, potentially, their baby. In rare cases, the pregnant woman or person might be affected by carbon monoxide by a faulty gas appliance in the home, so in that case the test might be life-saving. However, for those who smoke and who don't want to stop, they may feel that taking the test that shows they are a smoker, and then declining stop smoking services might be frowned upon or judged by the midwife. This can impact on the relationship between the midwife and woman/person. For those who do not smoke, they may object to being tested rather than being believed. This can also impact on the relationship between the woman/person and the midwife.

If you do want to stop, you can ask for support and a referral to a stop smoking service – you don't need to take the test for this to happen. If you are a non-smoker, you don't need to do the test to prove that this is true, but you can decide to do so if you wish to. If you are a non-smoker, but want to take the test to see if your body is being affected by passive smoking, or worrying amounts of CO from another source, you can choose to do this too.

* Most pregnant women and people have a 'dating scan' at about 12 weeks of pregnancy. The scan provides an estimated due date (EDD) which is the date at which the scan calculates 40 weeks of pregnancy. The scan is not necessarily accurate, and furthermore, every person's pregnancy is very different. Some women/people go into labour before 37 weeks without their baby showing signs of prematurity, or after 42 weeks without their baby showing signs of being 'overdue'. However, once the EDD is given, pressure to induce labour is likely to happen shortly after 40 or 41 weeks, with the risk that the baby is simply not yet ready to be born despite their estimated gestation date. This is an even higher risk if a medical condition means that the baby's birth is brought forward even earlier than 40 weeks (by induction or caesarean). Even though these babies are considered to be 'term', some babies are just not yet ready to be born and might have difficulties after birth. For further reading on these topics, see *aims.org.uk/rights*.

Making decisions about antenatal tests and checks

Now that you know that you can decide whether or not to have these and any other checks, you can also find out what the consequences of the results may be, before making your decision. Equally, you can simply let them happen – that's also your choice! There is no obligation to ask more questions. This is all in your control. You can choose to have some tests or checks and not others.

For some tests and checks you can decide you don't want them, and later change your mind. That's not the case for all of them as some need to be done at specific times in your pregnancy. Just ask!

Some ideas of things to ask:

- What information will this test give me?
- How accurate is it?
- What are the risks of having the test?
- How will the results affect the care that I am offered?
- Will it affect any recommendations for the timing of the birth?
- What are the risks of declining it?
- Do I have to decide right now?

If you decide to have a test and then are told that you 'have to' do something, or that you 'cannot' access a specific service due to the test results, remember that:

- You never *have* to do anything. You make the decisions. You can choose to accept the advice, or decline it, the choice is yours.
- Denying you a service based on a test result must be a proportional and reasonable response to the specific situation, and should be based on good medical evidence.

Screening and diagnostic tests

It is important to understand the difference between screening tests and diagnostic tests. The result of a screening test does not confirm that your baby has, or doesn't have, a syndrome or disease, but it gives an indication of what the chances are that they do or don't have one. Whatever the result, you will then have the option to consider a diagnostic test, which is a test which tells you almost certainly whether or not your baby has a particular chromosomal difference or illness. Chromosomal differences will be seen in Down's Syndrome, Turner's Syndrome and Patau Syndrome. They are sometimes called chromosomal disorders because they are due to an error in the replication of chromosomes before the egg and sperm combine, but people are not 'disorders', so the word 'difference' is used now.

An example of a screening test is the Nuchal Translucency Test (NT test), which is a combination of a blood test and ultrasound, and is routinely offered at around 10-14 weeks of pregnancy. It looks for signs of the three syndromes mentioned above – Down's Syndrome, Turner's Syndrome or Patau Syndrome. A computer analyses the results to give an estimated chance of the baby having any of these syndromes. The advantage of screening tests is that they are non-intrusive. The disadvantage is that they cannot give a definite answer but only a chance, for instance 1/150. (This means that 1 out of 150 babies will have the condition and 149 will not.)

There are two types of diagnostic tests that are used in pregnancy to detect whether a baby has a chromosomal difference: CVS (chorionic villus sampling) and amniocentesis. Diagnostic tests will tell you with almost 100% certainty whether or not your baby has any of the chromosomal differences which are looked for. These involve a needle being inserted through the pregnant woman or person's abdomen, into the uterus. The CVS test takes a tiny sample of the placenta, while the amniocentesis takes a tiny amount of amniotic fluid. These diagnostic tests do carry a small risk of miscarriage and how high this risk is depends on the skill and technique of the practitioner, so you can ask them about their experience and statistics before deciding. If you are pregnant with two or more babies you will need an expert in carrying out this test on twins or other multiples.

You can visit the NHS pages on CVS and amniocentesis here: *aims.org. uk/rights*.

Non-invasive Diagnostic Testing (NIPT) (also known as cfDNA screening)

There is a third type of test which looks for chromosomal differences, called the NIPT or sometimes the cfDNA test. Although this is a screening test, the company that offers it states that it is very accurate in predicting the chance of your baby having chromosomal differences.   It is not widely available through the NHS at this time but plans to implement it are in hand. It only involves the pregnant woman or person having a blood test, so it's a non-invasive test with no risk of miscarriage. It is widely available in the private sector for a few hundred pounds.

This screening test can still give false positives (that is it can suggest that the baby has a chromosomal difference when they don't) and false negatives (it suggests that the baby does not have a chromosomal difference when they do). CVS or amniocentesis tests are still considered to have a higher level of accuracy. You can find more information on the accuracy of the NIPT test *aims.org.uk/rights,* and the NHS page gives good details on what can happen and the decisions you can make: see *aims.org.uk/rights.*

You can talk to your midwife about what else may be looked for in each scan and test, and what tests may be available to you if you have a family history of a genetic difference.

Some people choose not to have any tests, screening or diagnostic, for chromosomal differences because, regardless of the results, they would continue the pregnancy anyway. Others are happy to accept the screening and then, if they are considered high risk, to be referred for a diagnostic test, whilst others want to have a diagnostic test anyway, in which case the screening text would not give any useful information.

If you find out that your baby has a chromosomal difference or serious health problem

If you discover that your baby has a chromosomal difference, or a serious health condition, you don't need to rush into any decisions. Take your time and don't be pushed into a decision, bearing in mind that if you feel that a termination may be the right option for you, there will be specific time limits. You can ask what these are so you know how long you have to think things through.

You will be offered discussions with a doctor and your midwife, but you might also want to talk to people who have experience of continuing with a similar pregnancy, and/or raising children with the same conditions or differences as yours. You might also want to talk to people who have chosen not to continue with their pregnancy. There are many charities and organisations which specialise in supporting parents who discover that their baby has a particular disability, health condition or difference and they can often put you in touch with families who have made a variety of choices.

Although midwives and doctors are often very supportive, many families report that it appears to be expected that the mother or pregnant parent will choose to terminate the pregnancy if certain differences are found. Sympathy is a common experience for many parents, where midwives and doctors say, "I'm sorry that your baby has XYZ condition..." which some parents feel lessens the joy they feel about their child.

You should have respectful, non-judgemental and compassionate care no matter what your decision is. If this is not how you are being treated you might want to point this out to the staff. Remember that you have the right to change your midwife or doctor. Adjusting to the fact that your baby has a chromosomal difference, disability or health condition can take time and it is natural for you to feel you are perhaps grieving for the baby you imagined and expected.

This pregnancy is still **your** pregnancy, the baby is still **your** baby, and your body is still **your** body. Some parents report feeling that the medical team 'took over', and decisions stopped being theirs, but decisions about pregnancy and birth still only belong to the pregnant mother or person.

You may like to read one woman's story of being a student midwife learning about supporting parents of babies with Down's Syndrome – and being the mother of a child with Down's Syndrome herself. *AIMS Journal Vol 29 No 2*, 'No tragedy to see here '– *aims.org.uk/rights*.

If you find out that your baby has a life-limiting condition

Sometimes, tests in pregnancy find that your baby appears to have a condition which may mean that your baby is unlikely to survive the birth or may have a limited life span afterwards. Sometimes these babies are described as 'incompatible with life' but many parents feel that this is not entirely accurate, as their baby lived, even if it was only for a short time.

In this situation you might be told that you have to have a specific type of birth, such as an induction or a caesarean, or be told that you have to birth in hospital. Sometimes this will be important for the health of your baby or for you, but it is not always the case. As always, you can ask questions until you're happy that you understand what is being offered and why, and make your own decision.

You should be provided with support to understand what may happen when your baby is born and what interventions may be offered, and why. Pain relief may be required because of the condition or because an intervention may cause distress or pain. Some parents will want every intervention possible to try to prolong their baby's life, whilst others will feel more comfortable just making sure their baby is made comfortable but otherwise letting nature take its course. Having a clear, agreed plan in advance of the various options which are most likely to be offered may help you to avoid having to make decisions in the moment, under stress. You can, of course, change your mind at any time if you want to, provided that you have parental responsibility.

The charity 'Together for Short Lives' helps families whose child may have a life-limiting or life-threatening condition. See *aims.org.uk/rights.*

Support organisations

Down's Syndrome Organisation
A charity to support parents of babies with Down's syndrome. This charity has a leaflet called 'Looking forward to your baby'.

Soft UK
A charity giving support and information for families affected by Trisomy 13, 18 and related conditions.

Positive about Down's Syndrome (PADS)
PADS' website is written by parents for new and expectant parents to share the reality of living with Down's syndrome in modern Britain. PADS provides information and support to pregnant parents and parents after birth and has two Facebook groups.

Antenatal Results and Choices
A charity which can support you in your decisions, especially if you decide to terminate your pregnancy.

The contact information for these organisations can be found at *aims.org.uk/ rights.*

Mid-pregnancy anomaly scan 18-21 weeks
This scan looks at the development of your baby and it is at this stage that the sonographer will look for a series of conditions both in the baby and also the uterus and placenta. An example of a condition looked for during this scan

is spina bifida, which affects the spinal cord. You can find more about the anomaly scan on the NHS website via *aims.org.uk/rights.*

You should have been given information explaining that this scan is primarily to find out whether your baby has one of the specific health conditions that can be seen at this stage of development. Therefore, you may wish to prepare yourself for the possibility – albeit small – that a condition may be found, and you might want to attend the scan with your partner, if you have one, or another supportive person. If no conditions are found on the scan it does not mean that your baby does not have a condition, disability or difference as not everything can be seen on a scan. Sometimes, the scan may pick something up that turns out to not be an issue at all (a 'false positive'), and this can lead to unnecessary stress and worry.

As with any test, you can decide whether or not you want to have this scan. It is optional and the only person who can decide if they want to accept the offer of the scan is the pregnant woman or person.

Finding out the sex of your baby

At this same scan offered at around 18-21 weeks, most sonographers will be able to tell parents the most likely sex of their baby, if they want to know, although they don't always get it right! It is sometimes not possible to tell due to the position of the baby. If you don't want to know the sex, just ask to not be told. If you want to know, you may need to ask. Some hospitals have a policy of not telling parents, and there is no specific right to know. You can choose to have a private scan to discover the likely sex if you want to.

If you have a CVS or amniocentesis these can tell you the sex of your baby with an extremely high level of accuracy.

Growth scans

As well as the two ultrasound scans routinely offered at around 10-14 weeks and around 18-21 weeks, you may be offered additional scans that aim to check your baby's growth. These used to be fairly rare, but it is becoming increasingly common for women to be offered growth scans.

Many women and people can then be put under pressure to accept an induction if their baby appears to be 'too big' or 'too small'. However, with the information and evidence that we have at the moment we don't know whether or not the benefits outweigh the risks of induction. We do know that growth scans can be unreliable, and that very often babies are born a completely different size to that estimated.

It is up to you whether or not you accept a growth scan. It's worth thinking about what the consequences might be and how you might deal with them. If you are offered induction following a growth scan, you might be told that your baby is at immediate risk unless you accept it. While this may be true in some cases, it is more common for babies to be fine without being induced. Induction may be able to reduce a risk by a small amount, but it comes with its own risks and consequences. Remember that you can keep asking questions, obtain a second opinion, and take the time to make the decision that's right for you.

The AIMS Guide to Induction of Labour explains the knowledge that we have about the benefits and risks of growth scans, and how they may impact on your care options. You can buy the book via the AIMS website, on Kindle or as a printed book – *aims.org.uk/rights*.

The Saving Babies Lives care bundle and other initiatives aimed at reducing stillbirth and other outcomes may be leading doctors and midwives to feel they need to persuade women and people to accept interventions including growth scans and induction, even where the evidence for them is very limited or even shows these interventions and tests to be harmful. This AIMS Journal article, 'First, do no harm' discusses the issue of care bundles and induction – *aims.org.uk/rights*.

Ultrasound and safety

Ultrasound in pregnancy was introduced without any long-term safety studies. It is now considered to be unethical to do these studies, so we cannot be certain that there are no adverse effects from ultrasounds in pregnancy, and the dramatically increased number of scans that women are being offered is concerning. Some studies of antenatal ultrasound have shown that it can cause brain changes, such as an increase in left-handedness. See *aims.org.uk/ rights*.

While left-handedness isn't in itself a concern, the fact that the brain is showing changes is a worry as other changes may be happening that we haven't yet seen. Anecdotally, some women report feeling their babies move away from the ultrasound probe as though it feels uncomfortable for their baby.

There remain concerns within medical circles about balancing what ultrasound can offer medically with any potential risk of exposure, particularly very early in a pregnancy or when the scan is being carried out for social and not medical reasons. See *aims.org.uk/rights*

As we have such little information, we cannot say with absolute certainty that ultrasound is safe or not safe. Some people decide that they want to avoid or minimise ultrasound exposure, including avoiding non-medical private scans, and minimising the use of a doppler (which listens in to your baby's heartbeat using ultrasound) at routine appointments. A pinard – a wooden trumpet-shaped device – can be used instead if desired, although with this instrument only the person using it, e.g. the midwife, can hear the baby's heartbeat.

While this may sound worrying, it is really important to remember that ultrasound has been used in pregnancy for years and nearly everyone you know who is under 50 will have been scanned before they were born.

Dr Sarah Buckley's website has more information about ultrasound in pregnancy – see *aims.org.uk/rights*.

Vaccinations in pregnancy

No vaccines can be tested on pregnant women, so all vaccines offered are on the basis that they are considered to offer more benefits than risks. Government agencies responsible for the safety of drugs monitor safety, which is not the same as holding clinical trials.

Any problems caused by any vaccine can be reported to the Medicines and Healthcare products Regulatory Agency (MHRA) through the Yellow Card scheme. Anyone can report a side effect from a vaccine (or any other medication) and if a side effect is reported to a GP they should report it. In theory, this should allow any adverse reactions in pregnant women or people to be recorded and the data analysed. In practice, as few people know that this scheme exists, and because milder side effects are rarely reported, the data may not be as complete as it should be.

You can find the Yellow Card reporting scheme on the MHRA website, via *aims.org.uk/rights*.

The decision about whether or not to accept vaccines belongs solely with the pregnant woman or person. We can choose to accept them or decline them. To help make the decision, there are some important things to consider.

For more information and resources about the pertussis (whooping cough) vaccinations during pregnancy, see the AIMS information page on vaccinations, and the NHS web page on the whooping cough vaccination in pregnancy at *aims.org.uk/rights*.

What is in the vaccine?

You have the right to read the insert that comes with the vaccine – which is the same type of insert that you have to get, by law, with any drug. You might wish to check to see if there are any ingredients that you are allergic to.

Some vaccinations are actually a combination of multiple ones. For instance, whooping cough is not available on its own, but only as one part of a vaccine which also includes vaccinations for polio, diphtheria and tetanus.

Summary

There is a common misunderstanding around health care which is that all tests or checks must be helpful otherwise they wouldn't be done. Of course, most are helpful to many, and there can be risks from not having the tests or checks. But there may also be risks involved in having them. To make an informed decision we need to know what the consequences to us might be of what we are offered in pregnancy – the pros and cons. This chapter did not aim to give you all the details of all of the pros and cons of the tests and checks that you may be offered in pregnancy. Instead, it aimed to explain why and how there might be risks as well as benefits to you, to help you to think about what's right for you.

Chapter 7

Preparation for your birth

When preparing for your birth you may be excited, or anxious, or both. Maybe you're scared, maybe you can't wait. You might feel differently about the whole thing every day. However you feel, knowing your options, knowing your rights and knowing more about how birth works can help you to feel more in control and reduce anxiety, and can also lead to a more positive birth. This chapter aims to help with all of this.

You might find this chapter useful for creating a birth plan, if you were thinking of having one. Birth plans are discussed in Chapter 3 (p.34).

Optimising your birth space

If you are planning to birth vaginally, probably the most important thing to plan for is how to most effectively support your body's own oxytocin production. Oxytocin is one of the hormones that is released in our bodies during birth. It is a hormone that is affected by our environment, and by how we feel towards the people around us.

Oxytocin is a key hormone for creating uterine contractions, which help to birth our baby (or babies) and their placenta, and it is an essential hormone for breastfeeding. Oxytocin produced within the body also helps us to release endorphins, our body's natural painkillers. It is known as the 'shy hormone' because it is easily suppressed if we feel stressed, scared or unsupported, which is why the people around us matter so much and why the environment we birth in matters too. There is a really good reason for this. As we birth our babies, we are the most physically vulnerable that we can be in our lives, other than in infancy. Back before we lived in houses, when we shared our spaces with animal predators, we would be in real danger if a large predator happened across us while we were in labour. Therefore, the hormone which drives labour can stop or slow down when we feel unsafe and, in times gone by, this would have given us time to get away to somewhere safer.

In modern times, we may not need to worry about bears or wolves crossing our path when we're in labour, but our bodies can react in just the same way if we feel worried or anxious. This may be triggered by bright lights and bleeping machines in hospital, a brusque or uncaring midwife, doctor or other birth attendant, by not having a midwife there if we want one, or even just by the travel to the birth centre or hospital. Think about how we'd care for a cat birthing kittens. We would let her find a quiet, dark space where she felt cosy and safe. We would keep an eye on her but normally we would avoid all interference unless needed. We wouldn't whisk her off to the vet at the first sign of labour, make her lie on a flat surface with bright lights shining down at her, strap monitors to her belly, and let the vet push their fingers inside her to 'check her progress'. We know what mammals need to birth well – a safe, calm space with dimmed lights, where they don't feel like they're being watched. We should give ourselves the same respect together with access to medical care if needed, and access to pain relief if wanted.

Some women find that being in hospital feels safe and reassuring. Others feel safer in different birth spaces, such as a midwife-led unit or home. The main point is that wherever you feel safest is likely to be the space where your body releases the most oxytocin.

Sometimes, we can't be in the place where we feel safest. You might have really wanted to have a homebirth or to use a midwife-led unit, but you later decided that a hospital birth is right for you for medical reasons. You might have conflicting feelings; for instance you may prefer to be closer to the doctors and feel safer at hospital, but find the environment makes you feel on edge. Whatever the situation, there is always value in working on creating a space that feels, as far as possible, safe and cosy, wherever that is, to encourage our bodies to release that incredible hormone.

For many people, feeling safe means having the right people around them. Midwife Ina May Gaskin says, "If a woman doesn't look like a goddess during labor, then someone isn't treating her right." Having a midwife that you know and trust (see 'Continuity of Carer' p.61) can be invaluable, but if you are meeting your midwife and doctor for the first time when you are in labour, how you feel about the way that they are supporting you can impact on your labour's progress, so remember that you can ask to change midwife or doctor if you want to. It might just be enough to ask them to do things like speak quietly and keep the lights low. A partner or trusted relative or friend can make a huge difference to you feeling safe and secure. Some women and people benefit from having a doula, ideally someone they've built a relationship with before labour starts.

You may be asked whether you are prepared to have students in the room with you. You can decide that you will agree to this or you can decide to not allow them to be there. If you allow them in but later want them to leave, this is also your right.

Other simple ways to create an oxytocin-boosting birth space, which can be done no matter where you give birth, include:

- Dimmed lights. Consider drawing curtains or blinds in the daytime and you can, if you wish, turn off the lights in the birth room.

- Having your own pillow, with your own scent to sink into, can make a medical environment feel more like home.
- Touch, if it feels right. Massage, stroking, hugging, kissing can all help to release oxytocin. Sometimes just having a loved one stroke your arm or back feels great. Sometimes birthing women and people detest being touched in labour. Go with what feels right for you and don't hesitate to ask for touch to start or stop.
- Aromatherapy oils may feel comforting and relaxing. Ensure that any used are safe for use in pregnancy and birth.
- Peaceful sounds. Ask those around you to keep their voices low and calm. Consider whether you want your own music choices, hypnobirthing tracks or other sounds.
- Some women and people like to have photographs of loved ones to look at, or birth affirmations, which are phrases and images that are supportive and encouraging.
- Easy to digest, energy filled food and drinks can help you to feel nurtured and nourished, as well as providing much needed energy. Drinks with a straw are far easier to drink than drinking from a cup when in labour, especially if you are in a forward leaning position. (See more about eating and drinking in Chapter 9 p.119.)

Think about how you might support each of your main senses – what you can touch or who touches you, what you can hear or listen to, what scents you can smell and what you might not want to smell, what you can see that makes you happy, and how you can support your oxytocin flow with lowered lights and refreshing or comforting things to taste.

Consider what you can use to offer physical support in your labour, to help you to keep upright and mobile (see next section). Special birth couches, chairs, slings and balls can be really helpful but are no means essential. Look at what you can lean over, or how you could use pillows and maybe a duvet to make a nest that you can rest against while on all fours.

No matter your choice of birth place you should be able to create the birth space that is right for you. If you are birthing in hospital or a midwife-led unit it is best to check in advance about what equipment can be brought in, as there will usually be limitations on equipment that needs to be plugged into the mains power. Battery powered electronics should be fine, as well as items such as battery powered electric tea lights. Usually hospitals allow mobile phones to be charged, but do check in advance.

Using complementary medicine

It is your right to use complementary medicine if you wish to. You don't need anyone's permission to do this. You will need to provide these yourself so bring them to your birth space. Add a note about what you want to use to your hand held notes if you have any, or if your notes are now electronic, ask your midwife to do so, so that your midwife or doctor are aware of any possible interactions with medicines that they may recommend.

Upright and active birth, and birth positions

If you are labouring rather than having a caesarean birth, lying on a bed on your back may make your labour longer, more painful and more likely to lead to complications than if you are able to be mobile, or at least forward-leaning (e.g. a supported kneeling position). Our bodies use pain as a way to communicate with us and we often feel the urge to move in labour, e.g. walking or swaying our hips. This is our body telling us that it needs us to move in a way that helps our baby or babies to be born. In turn this reduces the pain that we may be feeling. We don't have to be standing or walking to have an active labour. Sitting on a birth ball allows us to move our hips, and as labour progresses we can remain upright by leaning over the end of the bed (you could raise the bed if you wanted to stand on the floor), or the side of the birth pool, or make a nest out of pillows and lean forward over it. You can lean over anything in the room that's strong enough to hold you, it doesn't need to be the bed. There may be a sling, or other equipment to help you with this.

There are many different forward leaning positions and your midwife, or doula if you have one, should be able to help you to try different ones but ultimately what matters most is that you feel free to be in the position you want to be in, and to move as your body tells you to.

You might be asked or told to lie on the bed, but you don't have to. No one has the right to force you into any position. You might want to lie down, that's also your choice. Some birthing women and people do find that it feels right for them and if this is what your body is communicating with you, it's fine to go with it.

When you come to the point of pushing your baby out, you may again be asked to lie on the bed, but if you don't want to, you don't have to. Midwives are experienced at catching babies in all sorts of positions, or you can reach down and catch your own baby if you prefer. You do NOT need anyone's permission to catch your own baby! Lying on your back, however, will decrease the available space in your pelvis. As your baby passes through your pelvis, the pelvis flexes and opens a little more, especially at the back, and lying on your back prevents this from happening. Lying on your side can allow your pelvis to flex more than if you're on your back, and this might be a good position to try if you have an epidural (although some epidurals do leave you still able to get into forward leaning, kneeling positions, perhaps with support from pillows).

Deciding where and how you want to give birth

The actual location that you give birth in will affect what the surroundings are like, so choosing the place of birth that's right for you is important. We look at this in this section.

According to NHS guidance, women are supposed to be offered four different places of birth: home, freestanding midwifery unit (FMU), alongside midwifery unit (AMU) and hospital obstetric unit (OU, sometimes called a labour ward or delivery suite). Both FMUs and AMUs are midwifery-led, and are sometimes known as midwifery-led units (MLUs) or birth centres. Midwifery-led means that midwives will be the carers, with their expertise in supporting physiological birth as well as being highly skilled in resolving common birth complications. Women who are planning a caesarean birth will need to be on the obstetric unit.

Obstetric Unit

The Obstetric Unit (OU) is where people give birth in hospital. If you give birth on the OU you will have a midwife caring for you, and, if you need one, an obstetrician as well. Some services are only available on the OU, such as caesareans, and, usually, epidurals. Some OUs have a birth pool.

Midwife-led Units (FMUs and AMUs)

There are two types of midwife-led units (MLUs), freestanding midwifery units (FMUs) and alongside midwifery units (AMUs). An FMU is on a different site to the hospital, sometimes in a different town. Some rural parts of the UK that are geographically quite far from a central hospital have FMUs as an option, making them a great choice for women and people who do not want to travel far in labour, but who also don't want to have a homebirth.

An alongside midwifery unit (AMU) is typically 'alongside' or, at the very least, on the same site as, the hospital obstetric unit. They are often located right next to the OU so that if a person decides to be transferred to the OU (for instance, for an epidural, or in an obstetric emergency) then this can happen very quickly and easily. This could lead to the assumption that the AMU is safer than the FMU. Interestingly, however, this is not the case. Many of the outcomes looked at by the 'Birthplace Cohort Study 2011' showed that where birth was planned in the FMU, the outcomes were better than for births planned in the AMU, which in turn were better than for births planned in the OU. The initial data looked solely at women who were all classed as 'low risk' so the only difference was the planned place of birth. Subsequent analysis of the data looked at women who had specific medical conditions which meant that they were classed as 'high risk', and similar outcomes were shown, so the reason for the better outcomes outside hospital is *not* due to the fact that more women and people with medical conditions chose hospital as their preferred place of birth. See *aims.org.uk/rights.*

It is unclear why the outcomes in FMUs were better than AMUs, but it is extremely interesting that this is the case. It goes against what might be expected, as it might reasonably be assumed that being further away from the hospital (in an FMU) might lead to worse outcomes than being in the AMU which might be in the corridor next to the OU. And yet, this isn't the case – FMU outcomes, as shown in the Birthplace Cohort Study, are better than AMU outcomes.

Clearly, this is a complex issue which needs far more study. Medical treatments during birth save the lives of many mothers and babies who need them, but 'too much, too soon' can cause unnecessary harm, and this might be why planning to birth in the obstetric unit leads to worse outcomes than planning an out of hospital birth – interventions may happen too quickly, causing more harm than good. Equally, not treating a problem quickly enough can also cause harm so midwives need to be very skilled to be able to judge the right time to recommend further medical assistance, and when they can deal with a situation themselves.

It is worth pointing out again here that while you might be advised to be transferred from where you are (home, FMU, AMU) to the OU, you can, if you wish, decline to transfer. The decision is yours alone. If you are advised to transfer, you might want to use your decision-making tools (e.g. BRAIN on page 31) to decide what's right for you. Equally, you can transfer at any time if you wish. You don't *need* to go by ambulance from the FMU or from home, you can go in your own car if you have one, or someone else's car/taxi if you feel that it's safe to do so.

AMUs and FMUs are generally designed to offer a tranquil and calm space, which is known to help the birth hormones to flow and can lead to labour working more smoothly than the typically bright, medical environment of the obstetric unit. They often have equipment to help to support upright and active birth, such as slings, balls, birth pools and special birth couches.

There is no medical reason why the equipment found in many birth centres couldn't also be provided in the obstetric unit, and the environment on the OU converted to a more tranquil and relaxing space, where active and upright birth is the norm. However, where this has been attempted, the expected improvements in outcomes have not been as impressive as hoped, which highlights that there may be other problems within the obstetric unit that need to be addressed. Having said that, any attempts to make the OU less clinical looking and more relaxing and supportive of oxytocin flow and physiological birth are a good thing.

Giving birth in a birth centre means that you have access to equipment that you may like to use but that you might not have at home, and some people like the convenience of just being able to turn up without preparing the birth space, and leaving without having to clean up!

Not all areas have both an AMU and an FMU, and some have neither – so don't forget that you can try to access one in a region near you. If you want to give birth in an AMU or FMU, and you are being told you can't, we suggest that you write a letter to the midwife in charge of the unit asking for a comprehensive list of the reasons why they don't want you to have access to a unit. It can also be helpful to ask if there are additional issues that your midwife or doctor feels may arise in your labour, what, if anything, they feel that the hospital would offer to try to overcome these concerns that are not available in the birth centre, and the difference this may make to outcomes. You will then be in a clearer position to challenge each of the reasons if you want to. If you would like support with this, you can contact the AIMS helpline – see *aims.org.uk/rights*.

The NHS has some guidance on different places of birth – see *aims.org. uk/rights*.

Homebirth

You have the right in law to decide to birth at home and this isn't something that should be up for negotiation. We don't have to leave our own homes if we don't want to. In practice, some women and people find that they are asked to be 'signed off' for a homebirth, but the right to birth at home is, legally, a decision that only the pregnant woman or person can make.

This right to birth at home was brought to the European Court of Human Rights by a Hungarian woman, Anna Ternovszky. The court decided that women can choose, if they wish to, to birth at home rather than in a hospital or midwife-led unit. There are no limitations on this, so doctors and midwives cannot deny a woman a homebirth because of her 'risk status' or because her pregnancy has passed a certain date. This ruling applies to the UK even after leaving the EU as it relates to our membership of the Council of Europe, not membership of the EU.

For more information about the Ternovszky v Hungary ruling, visit *aims. org.uk/rights*.

Right to have a midwife attend a homebirth

There is no obligation to have a midwife or doctor there unless this is what the person giving birth wants, but most pregnant women and people do want a midwife to attend them, so while the right to give birth at home is clear, what is the right to have a midwife attend the birth?

In England, the Department of Health's 'Maternity Matters' document from 2007 states that a woman has the right to birth at home as part of its commitment to:

> '...the importance of providing high quality, safe and accessible maternity care through its commitment to offer all women and their partners, a wider choice of type and place of maternity care and birth.'

It went on to say that one of the National Guarantees was the right to a homebirth.

In Scotland, 'The Best Start' review states:

> 'All women should have an appropriate level of choice in relation to place of birth and there are a number of choices that should be available to all women in Scotland including birth at home, birth in an alongside or freestanding midwifery unit, and hospital birth.'

Wales' 'A Strategic Vision for Maternity Services in Wales' states:

> 'Each Local Health Board is expected to provide access to a range of services for women to give birth including at home.'

Northern Ireland's Regulation and Quality Improvement Authority advises pregnant women and people that:

> 'There are two main types of maternity care for women in Northern Ireland:
>
> a) Midwife-led care with the woman birthing at home or in a midwife-led unit.
>
> b) Consultant-led with the woman birthing in an obstetric unit (hospital).
>
> 'If you have had consultant appointments during your pregnancy, depending on your individual circumstances, you can still consider giving birth at home (or in a midwife-led unit). If you

choose homebirth, your care will be provided by skilled and experienced midwives.'

For the links to the above references, which explain your rights to have a midwife attend you at a homebirth, please visit *aims.org.uk/rights.*

In addition to these rights, the National Institute for Clinical Excellence (NICE) states in its guidance, 'Intrapartum care for healthy women and babies' to:

'Explain to both multiparous and nulliparous women that they may choose any birth setting (home, freestanding midwifery unit, alongside midwifery unit or obstetric unit), and support them in their choice of setting wherever they choose to give birth.'
See *aims.org.uk/rights.*

Although the NICE guidance specifically refers to pregnant women and people who would be classed as 'low risk', it is important to note that women and people with risk factors *still have the same right* to birth at home if they wish to.

Each country's guidance supports each person's right to give birth where they wish to, with a reasonable expectation for care to be provided at that location. It is therefore clear that every pregnant woman or person has the right to be attended by a midwife at home and, therefore, that a midwife should be provided.

Booking a homebirth can be found on the AIMS Birth Information page, *aims.org.uk/rights.*

Right to have a midwife attend a 'high risk' homebirth

In practice, many pregnant women and people are told that they are 'not allowed' to have a homebirth, due to their 'risk status', but this does not change their right in law to have a homebirth, and they have the same right to midwifery care at home as anyone else.

If a doctor or midwife tells you that you can't have a homebirth for medical reasons, you can, if you want to, remind them that they are not allowed to not allow you! However, it is worth working with them to try to ensure that you clearly understand their concerns, and to look at ways to reduce any risks at home. You might want to say something like,

> 'When you say I can't birth at home, I understand that what you mean is that you wouldn't recommend it. However, as you know, the only person who can decide is me. I really want to understand the issues that concern you, so can we talk through those to find out how we can minimise any risks at home.'

By stating clearly that you know the decision is yours, not theirs, but also being open to having them as part of your care team to plan a birth that reduces any chances of complications, hopefully they will recognise their importance as part of your supportive care team. There is no need to fight, or to justify your decision.

Care at home will be provided by midwives, so doctors have no part in the birth at home, and it needs to be arranged with the midwifery service. The midwifery staff may want to involve the doctors as part of the plan of care, but it is up to you to decide if this is right for you and there is no requirement for a homebirth to be 'signed off' by a doctor. The midwifery service is not controlled by doctors; midwives are autonomous practitioners and independent of the doctors.

Having said that, a good doctor may be a hugely important member of your care team if you and/or your baby have any medical needs that come under their remit. They may be able to help you to plan for ways to support these needs at home. If they discuss the information you may need to help you to make your decisions, and support you in what you decide, then this is wonderful. On the other hand, if you feel uncomfortable with how you're being spoken to, or upset by it, then listen to your instincts – this may not to be a conversation that will help you with your decisions – and you may want to consider asking to speak to someone else instead, or consider the other suggestions in Chapter 3 (p.24).

If you are told that no midwives are available when you go into labour

Sometimes women or people who have booked a homebirth are told, towards the end of their pregnancy, that there may not be a midwife available on the day, perhaps because of staff sickness or because 'too many women' are labouring at the same time. If you are told this before you go into labour, you may wish to put in writing to the Head of Midwifery, copying in the CEO of the hospital, that you are booked for a homebirth, that you therefore expect to have midwifery care at home, and that any necessary adjustments to the midwifery schedule need to be made in advance to ensure that you can have a midwife attend you. You might point out that many hospitals have taken independent midwives onto their books on a temporary basis in order to provide additional cover. Including the reference above, explaining your rights to midwifery care at home for your relevant UK country, can also be helpful.

If you are actually in labour and you are told that a midwife is not available, it can be a very stressful situation so the first thing to remember is that very often this can be overcome. If you possibly can, have someone else deal with the situation so that you can focus on your job – having your baby – and they can do all the negotiating. The 'you' in the next few paragraphs is speaking to whoever is supporting you.

You are not responsible for the hospital's staffing issues, but do remember that neither is the person who answers the phone, so it is important to remain polite and positive with them – but also persistent. If they are not able to help you, then talk to them about who they can put you through to who is more senior. Take notes about who you speak to and when, but be kind and ensure that they understand that you are not taking their name to threaten them, but just so you have a record of who you have spoken to, and what their job role is.

Using the 'stuck record' technique is usually the most effective way to persuade the hospital to find a midwife (see Chapter 3 p.24). For example, phrases like: "She is in labour and has booked a homebirth with you and will be staying at home. Please can you send a midwife." – and repeat as needed!

"Please could you put me through to someone more senior. She is in labour and has booked a homebirth and will be staying at home."

"She has decided that she will continue with the homebirth that she has booked with you, so she will require a midwife as promised."

You might want to discuss how far through labour the labouring woman or person is, and pointing out that travelling to the hospital may lead to a birth in the car can encourage a greater speed of attendance! Keep going, be persistent but always ensure that you are following the wishes of the person giving birth. If they want you to keep trying, keep trying. If they decided to transfer to hospital, then support them to do that.

If the person you are speaking to is not being supportive, consider asking to be put through to someone else (or find a way to speak to someone else – i.e. side step around the wall (see Chapter 3, p.24).

It is quite common for an ambulance to be called if the hospital is struggling to find a midwife, but it is entirely the birthing woman or person's decision as to whether or not they accept this. There is no obligation to let the paramedics into the house, or to go with them to hospital.

Remember that a paramedic is not a midwife and they do not have midwifery training. According to the law they would not be able to perform clinical midwifery care except in the case of an emergency. In the situation where a homebirth was booked and a hospital refused to send a midwife, it might be argued that because an emergency situation could have been foreseen, the hospital was negligent in its duty to not send an appropriately trained healthcare provider.

Freebirth

A woman or person has the right to birth where they want to (provided they have the right to be in that location – for instance, they're not trespassing on private land) and to allow whomever they want into their birth space. No one is required to have any form of birth attendant with them at their birth if they don't want to have someone there.

Freebirth is the decision to birth without the attendance of a registered midwife, doctor or other healthcare provider, such as a paramedic. Freebirth is legal in the UK. However, sometimes women and people will be threatened with, or referred to, Children's Services (Chapter 4 p.36) solely for planning or having a freebirth. The Royal College of Midwives (RCM) has stated,

'It is not appropriate for health professionals to refer a woman to social services with concerns about the unborn baby, solely on the basis that she has decline medical support, as she is legally entitled to do.' See *aims.org.uk/rights*.

AIMS considers that the term 'Freebirth' does not correctly describe the situation where a woman or person is abandoned to birth alone. For example, where a hospital has refused to send out a midwife when one was requested, that woman or person is not freebirthing; they have been abandoned.

Sometimes pregnant women or people are told that it is illegal to only have lay people at their birth, i.e. people who are not midwives or doctors, and they might be told that anyone being at the birth may be breaking the law, including the baby's father or other parent. This is not true. The law states that only a registered midwife or medical practitioner can 'attend' a woman in childbirth. In this case, 'attend' refers to providing clinical care, rather than simply being in the room. It is legal for a partner, friend, relative or doula to be at the birth of a baby where there is no medical care provider, but they cannot provide clinical care other than 'in a case of sudden or urgent necessity'. See *aims.org.uk/rights*.

If you are considering freebirthing, you may find the AIMS Birth Information page on Freebirth to be helpful: *aims.org.uk/rights*.

Another excellent resource is Birthrights' information sheet on freebirth: *aims.org.uk/rights*.

Labouring and giving birth in water

Most midwife-led units and many obstetric units have birth pools. Water can be a powerful form of pain relief and comfort in labour. It doesn't work for all, but the beauty of water is that if it doesn't work for you, you can just get out of the pool. Planning a waterbirth gives you complete flexibility, you can simply try it and see.

If you would like to have a waterbirth in the MLU or OU, you may find that there are restrictions in the hospitals guidelines. Remember that guidelines are not rules. While you do not have the absolute right to access a birth pool on the hospital's premises, there needs to be a strong medical reason for access to be denied.

If you are told that you cannot use the hospital's birth pool, ask for the full list of reasons, in writing if need be, so that you know what you need to negotiate, if that's what you decide to do. The AIMS helpline can support you with this. There are AIMS Journal articles which look at negotiating access to a birth pool for women and people who are having an induced labour, and for those who are told that they cannot have a waterbirth due to their BMI. See *aims.org.uk/rights* for these articles and information on how to access the AIMS helpline.

Waterbirth at home

If you are birthing at home, you have the absolute right to use a pool if you want to. No one can tell you that you're allowed, or not allowed to use equipment in your own home, including when you can get in or out of the pool. Sometimes women or people find that the water slows their labour, especially if they get in early on in labour, but this is not necessarily a bad thing and may make labour calmer and more peaceful. Water can be a powerful form of pain relief and comfort and you have the right to use it as you wish.

You also have the right to have the water at the temperature that is right for you. Very hot water can affect the baby's heart rate. NICE guidelines recommend that it is not above 37.5 degrees for this reason, although the evidence for this recommendation is not strong See *aims.org.uk/rights*.

When planning your home water birth, it might be helpful to plan for the *very rare* situation of not being able to get out of the pool by yourself. Shockingly, we've been told that midwives are sometimes instructed to tell pregnant women and people that, in the case of emergency, an inflatable birth pool will need to be cut open to get you out quickly. *This is very dangerous and should never happen.*

Bursting the pool would deflate it very quickly, but it would cause the water to flood out, and anyone in the pool would be carried out with it in an uncontrolled way, possibly towards the person holding the knife or scissors used to burst the pool! Another serious risk is that it would be very likely to reach electrical equipment which would lead to the risk of electrocution, or the electricity in the property going off at the breaker, perhaps plunging everyone into darkness at the moment of an emergency.

The correct procedure in the case of emergency is to open the valve of the centre ring of the pool, which will allow the pool sides to lower while retaining most of the water, and keeps the structural integrity of the pool. At this point the woman or person can be more easily assisted out of the pool, if necessary, and the remaining water will maintain buoyancy to help with this. If the woman or person is unconscious or losing consciousness and cannot be lifted out, a birth attendant or partner should get into the pool and hold the woman or person's head above water until additional paramedic help arrives.

Midwives usually visit your home before the birth, and this visit will generally include a risk assessment, including an assessment of your plans for using a birth pool. This would be a good opportunity to ensure that your midwife is up to date with the appropriate way to deal with an emergency in an inflatable birth pool. You may find the guidance from the Health and Safety Executive (HSE) to be useful. It states:

'Bursting the pool is not an option to reach the mother in an emergency due to the large volume of water.'

To read the full guidance from the HSE, visit their web page on manual handling risks for midwives attending waterbirths via *aims.org.uk/rights*.

Caesarean birth

If your doctor considers that there is a medical need for you to have a caesarean birth, and you agree to it, this will be arranged for you. If you want to give birth by caesarean but a doctor does not agree that there is a medical need, you should still be able to have one. NICE Guidelines on caesarean section (CS) state:

> 'For women requesting a CS, if after discussion and offer of support (including perinatal mental health support for women with anxiety about childbirth), a vaginal birth is still not an acceptable option, offer a planned CS.' See *aims.org.uk/rights*.

Despite this guidance, some doctors will not support women to have a caesarean without what they consider to be a medical reason. If you find yourself in this situation, try referring them to the NICE guidelines and asking (perhaps in writing) why they are not following them. If the issue is with a specific doctor, that doctor should refer you to another doctor according to NICE guidelines.

> 'An obstetrician unwilling to perform a CS should refer the woman to an obstetrician who will carry out the CS.' See *aims.org.uk/rights*.

If you continue to have an issue getting your needs met, then putting this in writing may help. If the issue is hospital policy, we would recommend that you write to the CEO of the hospital to state that they are not offering the service that you need, and/or to the person or people who are responsible for commissioning your local maternity services to ask why this service is not being commissioned. Sometimes the name of the maternity commissioner is online, and you can find it by searching online for 'maternity commissioner' and the name of your hospital. If you can't find yours, search for a general email address and write to the commissioners at your local Clinical Commissioning

Group. Again, you can find the details by searching online for the term Clinical Commissioning Group and the name of your hospital.

Don't forget that the AIMS helpline is there to support you – see *aims.org. uk/rights*.

Gentle caesareans

Gentle caesareans, sometimes called 'natural caesareans', are simply a range of measures that may help a caesarean birth to be more positive, enjoyable and safe. There is no complete list of what makes a caesarean 'gentle', but the term is helpful if you wish to search online for ideas and experiences. Of course, not all of these ideas can be used in the case of an emergency, but many can, even when the caesarean wasn't planned in advance.

Common ideas are:

- Who would you like to be in the room? Some Trusts will be happy to allow more than one birth partner, but this is likely to need to be negotiated in advance and still may not be supported on the day. There is no specific right to this, but the reasons that are often given, such as lack of space, are rarely supported in fact; often students are invited in (you have the right to say you don't want them to be there) and there's space for them! This means that you do have room for negotiation here.

- Remember that you do have the right to ask people to leave if you wish. You have the right to decide whether or not students are permitted to watch, or to do any part of your surgery.

- Do you want your own music to be played? Your own choice of radio station or hypnobirthing tracks playing in the theatre? Nothing at all?

- Would you like the staff to not chitter chat but to keep quiet, while keeping you informed about what is happening? Some women and people prefer it if the midwives and doctors just chat amongst themselves as it can help them to feel that this is just another normal day, which for some people can reduce anxiety.

- Some hospitals use clear drapes between the mother or birthing parent's head and their abdomen so that they can see the baby being born. Others will drop the drapes at this point for the same reason. It is not possible for the mother or birthing parent to see the incision as the bump is still in the way.

- Rather than pulling the baby out, give them time to wriggle out of the incision themselves once they are partly born. This can be a slower transition to outside life for the baby than the conventional caesarean method.

- Baby being placed skin to skin with their mother or birthing parent as soon as they are born. This means that the gown needs to have an opening at the front. It also means that the ECG (heart monitoring) pads need to be placed on the mother or birthing parent's sides or their back, so that they don't interfere with the baby.

- Any IVs to be placed in the mother or birthing parent's non-dominant arm so that they can more easily hold their baby.

- Delayed cord clamping. Because optimal cord clamping can take an hour or so to fully "wait for white", this is not feasible in theatre. However, it is perfectly reasonable to wait for several minutes.

- Breastfeeding or chestfeeding in the theatre, if that is right for you.

Many of these ideas will increase your body's own oxytocin. In a caesarean birth, artificial oxytocin is used to contract the uterus after birth, but raising your natural birthing hormone will be beneficial, too. This natural oxytocin will help the uterus to contract, help with breastfeeding or chestfeeding if you plan to (which releases more oxytocin – a virtuous circle), and help with bonding with your baby. Holding your baby skin to skin and breastfeeding or chestfeeding are the two most important ways to trigger your own oxytocin. In addition, remembering that oxytocin is actually inhibited by fear and anxiety (see Chapter 7 p.81), feeling calmer and more in control means that we are supporting what oxytocin we already have in our bodies even if we are unable to stimulate extra oxytocin production.

There are many other ways to make a caesarean birth more positive, so do talk to other people online and in person for ideas.

Ideally, talk to your midwife and doctor in advance about what is important to you and write it in your birth plan, even if you are not planning a caesarean birth. Many doctors and midwives welcome these ideas, some will need some persuasion and sometimes you may need to negotiate hard for them. This is much more easily done during your pregnancy than when you are in labour, or in hospital for your caesarean.

Guidelines and policies (both national and local)

Guidelines (sometimes known as policies) are documents which are created in an attempt to ensure that care is offered equitably and appropriately: the right treatment for the right condition. Guidelines are based on both evidence and opinion. There are a number of organisations which write medical guidelines, and you might find any or all of them suggested to you in any particular situation. The most commonly used are NICE (National Institute for Health and Care Excellence) which have been developed to guide practice in the NHS in England, Wales and NI. Scotland has different guidance produced by SIGN. There are also guidelines produced by RCOG (Royal College of Obstetricians and Gynaecologists), RCM (Royal College of Midwives) and it is common for NHS Trusts or Boards to develop their own. You can obtain the hospital's own guidelines from your midwife or doctor, or via your hospital's PALS service. PALS stands for 'Patient Advice and Liaison Service' and every hospital should have this service. You should be able to find their contact details on your hospital's website.

You will find links to NICE, RCOG, RCM and SIGN on our website at *aims.org.uk/rights*.

It is commonly believed that we have research evidence to answer most medical questions, but often the evidence either does not exist or is not of good quality. Even if there is good quality research evidence there may be limitations on what the study was able to look at. When guidelines are created, the aim is to use the best quality evidence available, but if only poor-quality evidence exists then that may be used. This therefore means that the guidelines may themselves be of good quality or poor quality. In practice, many guidelines are a mixture of both good- and poor-quality evidence, and where there is insufficient or missing evidence, the opinion of those creating the guidelines will be used. In an attempt to make this clearer, some organisations mark each section of their guidelines to show what level of evidence is used when writing it, or whether no evidence is used and the section is based on opinion. NICE includes the research evidence in the full guideline rather than the short version.

When we talk to our midwife or doctor about our birth plan, we might be told that something we are considering having or not having is 'against guidelines'. Guidelines are not rules or laws. Pregnant and birthing women and people do not have to follow them, and neither do doctors and midwives. However, should a midwife or doctor go 'off guidelines' (meaning that they support a woman or person to accept or decline care which does not follow the guideline) they may be asked to justify this. If they have explained the benefits and risks to the person in their care appropriately, and supported their decision, this should not be a problem for them. Unfortunately, in practice it still can be, but that's an issue with the management of the maternity services and is not something that individual women or people are responsible for. But this explains why there is often so much pressure to get women and people to adhere to guidelines. Again, we are not responsible for the management of the maternity services, we are only responsible for our own bodies and our own babies.

If you are told that something that you want to do or not do is going against guidelines, feel free to ask your midwife or doctor for a copy of the guideline that they're referring to. You have a right to see them and to have a copy, without charge. You may find that what you are wanting is not actually 'against guidelines' after all! You might want to check the date of the guidance, and when it is due for review so that you can ask if there is any more up to date research which has not yet been considered. You can ask for guidelines on any area of your care (or other subjects, if you're interested) and you can access RCOG, RCM, SIGN and NICE's guidelines online, for free. By reading it yourself it might help you to decide whether what you are being *offered* is right for you. As always, you can continue to ask questions if you want more information. Note that both NICE and RCOG provide a version of their guidelines for clinicians, and a simplified version for the public. Although the latter can be easier to understand, they can sometimes downplay how weak the evidence can sometimes be for a recommendation, compared to the clinician's version.

This is not intended to downplay the value of guidelines. They can be extremely helpful, and are very often based on high quality evidence. The important thing to know is that you don't *have* to follow them, if you don't want to, they're not *your* rules.

Sometimes you might be offered an intervention that actually contradicts the hospital's own guidelines, or the guidelines of other organisations. An example might be that you are told that you should have an induction at a certain date of your pregnancy even though the NICE guidelines might state that in your situation induction should not be offered until later. You might also not be advised that the guideline states that induction is only one of a number of options, including regular monitoring – or doing nothing. Or you might be denied treatment that you wish to have. For instance, as discussed above, you may wish to have a caesarean for non-medical reasons. The guideline might state that your hospital would support a caesarean in your situation, but the doctor refuses. In these situations, having the guidelines to hand can help you to understand what *should* be offered, and you can use this to help you to negotiate what's right for you.

AIMS books will always contain references to national guidelines where appropriate and explain their value or otherwise, depending on the subject.

Medical treatment outside hospital

If you had planned to birth at home or at a FMU or AMU, but are advised to birth in hospital because you need, or might need, a specific medical intervention or treatment, it might be possible for this intervention or treatment to be done at home or in the birth centre. For instance, women who decide to accept the offer of intravenous antibiotics, because of testing positive for Group B Strep in pregnancy or prolonged rupture of membranes, have been able to obtain support for this to be provided at home. So it is worth discussing with your midwife or asking to speak to a more senior midwife to see if they are prepared to offer some types of care outside the hospital.

It can help to reach out on social media to find other women who have experienced this and have negotiated this care, to show your hospital that other hospitals are willing to do this or, perhaps, that your own hospital has done this for someone else. Of course, you can also decide to decline the intervention or treatment that is offered, if you feel that this is the right decision for you.

For more information on Group B Strep see our website – *aims.org.uk/ rights.*

Summary

Planning your birth space can make a huge difference to your birth, whether you birth in your own home, the hospital's obstetric unit or in a midwife-led unit. Who you have with you and what your surroundings are like can influence the hormones that help birth to work well. You have a lot of control over who is with you and what your environment will be like, so it's well worth making it as close to ideal for you as possible.

Being upright and moving in labour, or using forward-leaning positions, can really help labour to progress well, and the only person who can decide how they want to move is you. You may be told that you have to remain still, but you don't. You have as much right to tell the midwife or doctor to lie on their back on the bed as they have to tell you to do so!

Chapter 8

Approaching the time of your baby's birth

About due dates

In our culture, there's a huge focus on the 'due date', which is sometimes written as 'EDD' meaning 'Estimated Due Date', and refers to the first day of the 40th week of pregnancy. You may also hear the phrase 'full term' or 'term'. This refers to the period of time from the start of the 37th week to the start of the 42nd week of pregnancy.

Estimating your due date is almost always done at your first visit to your midwife, who will ask you if you know the date of the first day of your last period. Using a formula known as Naegele's Rule, which was developed in the 1700s, your due date will then be estimated. This calculation assumes that every woman or person's menstrual cycle is 28 days long, and that every natural pregnancy length is the same – neither of which is true. Read more about Naegele's Rule here: *aims.org.uk/rights*.

The due date, 40 weeks of pregnancy, may then be 'confirmed' by your first scan, if you have one. However, it is still a guess. Every pregnancy is unique, and every baby is ready to be born at a different point during pregnancy. Only about 5% of babies are born on their due date. Babies are said to be full term between 37-42 weeks – a range of 5 weeks – so picking one arbitrary date does not make any sense and yet this is the date our culture focuses on to the point of obsession. The concept of babies being full term between 37-42 weeks is also not based on science. Many babies are born safe and happy before 37 weeks, clearly ready to be born. Some are born at 38 weeks or later showing signs of prematurity. Other babies are born at 42, 43 or 44 weeks of pregnancy and are clearly just the right gestation for them. 37-42 weeks is considered to be 'normal' but, in reality, it is just an average time when most babies arrive, nothing more.

Some pregnant women or people know for absolute certain when they conceived. Conception can happen a few days after sex, so that could explain some differences between a person's own dates and the scan, but for some women or people there is no doubt that the scan date is wrong. For instance, it might calculate that the baby was conceived several days before a woman or person had sex or inseminated. It might show the date of an assisted pregnancy to be quite different to the date that embryos are implanted.

If you are confident that your due date is incorrect, you can, if you wish, write this on your hand held notes, if you have paper notes. If your notes are electronic, you can ask your midwife to add your own due date as additional information. This may or may not be 'accepted' by your midwife or doctor. It also still focuses on the 'due date', so remember that the due date doesn't really have much meaning and you are not 'due' on the day that you hit 40 weeks.

The due date sets the dates of nearly everything that is then offered in your pregnancy journey. For instance, the 20-week scan and, if your pregnancy seems to continue for longer than the average, the date when you might be pressured to accept induction. If you know that your pregnancy is less advanced than the scan date then this might affect your decision making about whether or not to accept induction – or perhaps you would accept it, but you would want to wait longer than your midwife suggests. It can also affect what you decide to do if, for some medical reason, you are advised to have your baby before or shortly after 37 weeks, say. If, by your own dates, your 'due' date is earlier than the scan date, you may wish to consider waiting a little longer to reduce the chance that your baby will be premature. Of course, these decisions will depend on the situation at the time, and whether your baby would be better off being born immediately even if there was a risk of prematurity. You can see more at 'How accurate is my due date?' in the Birth Information pages on the AIMS website – *aims.org.uk/rights*.

Going into labour before 37 weeks

Some hospitals say that they will not support a homebirth or access to the Midwife-led Unit (MLU) before 37 weeks, and AIMS often hears from women or people who are classed as 36 weeks pregnant plus a few days and are worrying that they won't have the birth that's right for them because of this. There is nothing in law that endorses this, although they might argue that because the baby is more likely to require medical assistance after birth, it is best to be in hospital in the obstetric unit.

However, you are free to ask for some flexibility to have a midwife attend you at home or to access the MLU if you are likely to go into labour before 37 weeks. If the hospital considers that homebirth before 37 weeks of pregnancy is putting the baby at risk, it could be argued that they are putting the baby at even more risk by not attending. Given that 'due dates' are not accurate then attendance at homebirths before 37 weeks should be considered on a case by case basis. For instance, if a woman has a history of birthing healthy babies before 37 weeks, this might be a strong argument for her to have attendance at home.

Babies born before 37 weeks are classed as premature although, as I've already mentioned, the estimate of the due date is not very accurate, so it's not possible to know whether a baby really is premature unless after birth they show signs of not yet being ready to be born. Some will need help at birth because of their prematurity, and others will be completely fine. It is often, but not always the case, that the more prematurely a baby is born, the more assistance they are likely to need.

Going into labour after 42 weeks

'Post dates' means being pregnant for longer than 42 weeks (remembering that we cannot be at all confident of how accurate this is). In some hospitals they start to refer to being 'post dates' even earlier than this, with pressure being put on women and people to accept an induction at 40 or 41 weeks solely because of dates rather than medical indication.

Many babies (around 1 in 20) will be born after 42 weeks if left to their own devices, yet a common question pregnant women and people hear from family and friends is "How long will they let you go?" This is what I want to discuss here.

As you will already know if you've read the earlier chapters in this book, the only person who can legally decide what happens to your body is you. Therefore, any doctor or midwife who tells you that you "have to" be induced is not telling you the truth. "How long will they let you go?" is a really interesting question, because it implies that the control over your body is in the hands of the hospital, which of course it is not. It is actually saying that the hospital staff are the ones who decide what happens to you. But in that case, what would happen if you declined? Would you be dragged to hospital by the police? Of course not! The decision is yours and yours alone.

So, now that you know that it's up to you to make the decision about whether to be induced for being pregnant longer than the hospital's guidelines recommend, it's very important to have good information to make the decision with. The AIMS book, *The AIMS Guide to Induction of Labour, Chapter 2*, '*Reasons for induction of labour, Length of pregnancy*', goes into far more detail than there's space for here, and the AIMS website also has useful articles and information.

The main reason that induction is offered for a longer than average pregnancy is the fear about stillbirths. AIMS has analysed the data from MBRRACE, the organisation which looks at deaths of babies and women in the UK during pregnancy, birth and the following year. The data was collected from millions of women and babies over a ten year period, and, remarkably, it shows that stillbirth rates actually *drop* after 42 weeks! This data will reflect that babies considered at risk would be more likely to have been born earlier than 42 weeks, but if you need to consider whether to accept an induction solely because your pregnancy has continued longer than whatever the hospital guidelines are, and your baby seems to be otherwise well, this might be helpful to know.

You can read more about the AIMS analysis of the MBRRACE data on our website. See *aims.org.uk/rights*.

Before making a decision on whether or not to accept induction of labour for any reason you may wish to learn more about the benefits and risks of the induction process. It is a legal requirement for doctors to offer to explain the risks and benefits of any medical intervention, and induction is no different. While induced labour can lead to a very positive experience for some, it is a highly medicalised procedure which is significantly different to physiological labour and can lead to other medical interventions.

For a comprehensive look at the evidence on induction of labour, and ways to help you decide what's right for you, see the AIMS book *The AIMS Guide to Induction of Labour*, available in printed or Kindle format. See *aims.org. uk/rights*.

If you decide that you don't want to have an induction, you do not need to persuade your doctor or midwife to agree with your decision. You don't need to persuade them of anything because you are in control of this process, not them. You don't need to go to see them armed with your evidence, unless you want to. You can simply say that you don't wish to be induced. If they persist, you can politely remind them that the decision is yours alone, you have stated your decision and you have the right to have it respected. You can decide to have monitoring of your baby as outlined in the NICE guideline below if you want to, and this can help to give you an indication of your baby's well-being.

The NICE guideline on Induction of Labour states:

- 'If a woman chooses not to have induction of labour, her decision should be respected. Healthcare professionals should discuss the woman's care with her from then on.
- 'From 42 weeks, women who decline induction of labour should be offered increased antenatal monitoring consisting of at least twice weekly cardiotocography and ultrasound estimation of maximum amniotic pool depth.'

See *aims.org.uk/rights*.

Can I change my mind?

You can choose to decline an induction today, and change your mind tomorrow. Or next week. Or anytime. You can accept the offer of a booking for an induction, and then cancel it. All of this is in your control. If you feel under pressure, or that you are being coerced, you can state how you feel. For instance, you could say, "I feel that you are putting me under undue pressure to accept this intervention that you are offering. I have made my position clear, and I will tell you if I change my mind."

If you request an induction

If you request an induction, you will most likely be given lots of information about the risks. This is ironic as many women report that they are rarely told about any of the risks of the induction process when they are offered an induction (despite the legal obligation on the doctor to offer to do so as part of their requirement to ensure, if you accept the intervention, that you know all of the benefits and risks that may be important to you). However, if you wish to proceed, especially if you are post 40 weeks, there are ways to ensure a request for an induction is more likely to be supported. Have a very clear explanation of your reason or reasons, in writing. Reasons which can be categorised as medical may hold more sway, even if they are less important to you than social or other reasons. Unless you are already under the care of a doctor and can speak to them directly, you will initially need to speak to your midwife and ask her to refer you to a doctor. Although induction is a medical intervention, the midwifery team may be able to influence this for you, so if your midwife is in agreement with you this may really help. Remember that you can always contact one of the Professional Midwifery Advocates, the Head of Midwifery or a Consultant Midwife if your hospital has one. If a doctor will not agree to support an induction, you can ask to speak to another, more senior doctor.

The NICE Guidelines on Induction of Labour state:

> 'The GDG [Guideline Development Group] considered the dialogue between the woman and the clinician in making any decision about management to be important, and a case-by-case approach, taking into account the woman's clinical and personal circumstances, is appropriate.'

The same section goes on to state:

'Induction of labour should not routinely be offered on maternal request alone. However, under exceptional circumstances (for example, if the woman's partner is soon to be posted abroad with the armed forces), induction may be considered at or after 40 weeks.' See *aims.org.uk/rights*.

Some women have a very strong feeling that something is wrong and that their baby needs to be born. If your instinct is telling you this, listen to it, and try to communicate this clearly to your midwife or doctor. Many people are very tuned into their bodies and that instinct is very often right, so if this is how you feel, be persistent and clear until you are heard.

Do note that inductions are not always successful, and they are not always fast. Before making your decision, it is worth really understanding the process and options, how it may change your birth preferences and how to make the induction as positive as possible. We recommend the AIMS book, *The AIMS Guide to Induction of Labour* for more information. See *aims.org.uk/rights*.

Stretch and sweep

A stretch and sweep, sometimes called a sweep, is a form of induction that has risks as well as benefits and you can ask your midwife for information about these – or read the AIMS book *The AIMS Guide to Induction of Labour* – before deciding. I am also just going to add at this point that it is illegal for anyone to do a (consented) vaginal examination and then do a "stretch and sweep while I'm in there" without getting your consent in advance, as these are two separate medical procedures. A sweep done without your consent is criminal assault and battery.

If you are offered a sweep, you can choose to accept or decline it. If you want to have a sweep, there is no right to have it as such. In some situations, midwives will do one at 37 weeks of pregnancy, although usually they will want to wait until around the time of your due date because of the risks associated with sweeps and with early induction. Furthermore, sweeps are unlikely to be an effective form of induction unless a person is close to going into labour anyway. If you would like to research this further, our website has useful signposts to information and evidence at *aims.org.uk/rights*.

Having an induction of labour and a homebirth

Some women decide to have a sweep (see above) if they are planning a homebirth. Provided the sweep doesn't accidentally lead to the woman's membranes being ruptured (which can lead to a higher chance of infection, and possibly the need for medical intervention), a sweep is not a form of induction which should affect a homebirth. The most common risk of sweeps, other than the pain that they can cause while they're being done, is that they can lead to painful contractions that do not progress into active labour. This can be very tiring and can lead women to decide to transfer to hospital for additional pain relief.

What is normally referred to as 'induction' (meaning some combination of prostaglandin gel or pessary or mechanical dilation, artificial rupture of membranes and a Syntocinon drip) can lead to some serious outcomes such as the uterus becoming over-stimulated, causing distress to the baby, or, rarely, uterine 'rupture', as well as other serious consequences. Artificial rupture of the membranes can lead to infection, as well as an increase in pain. Rarely, it can cause a cord prolapse if the baby's position is too high, leaving space for the cord to slip past their body and through the cervix. This is a medical emergency. Because of these risks, this type of induction is usually done in hospital.

Outpatient inductions

However, some Trusts support what they call 'out-patient inductions'. This means that the pregnant woman or person attends the hospital for the pessary, gel or manual dilation device, and is offered monitoring for a period of time to try to tell whether the pregnant person or their baby are being adversely affected by the process. After a period of time, if all is well and the baby seems happy, the woman or person may be supported to leave the hospital and go home to wait for active labour, or for a period of time agreed with the hospital. In some cases, they are supported to stay at home for the remainder of their labour. If this feels like something that you would like to explore, don't hesitate to speak to your midwife or doctor about it.

Remember that hospital isn't a prison, and you can leave at any time if you wish to. However, if you are considering this type of induction and you wish to go back home, it is important to remember that these are very powerful drugs and your labour is no longer working solely with your body's own hormones. *Your body really could need more help once labour is started artificially.* The drugs used can also cause serious side effects to both you and your baby, so it is important that you understand what may be happening to your body before making the decision that's right for you.

Homebirth and birth centre access after 42 weeks

Many hospitals try to refuse to allow women access to a birth centre or support at homebirths after 42 weeks but hospitals are not legally able to decline this care solely because of this reason. Hospitals have to offer their service equitably, and they must have a justifiable reason to decline care. There is no medical reason to give birth in hospital solely because your baby is being born after 42 weeks.

Even if the birth centre's guidelines about who can access the unit state that people cannot use the birth centre if they are over 42 weeks pregnant, they are still obliged to justify denying access to it, and the justification must be a real medical reason. If this becomes an issue, do contact the AIMS helpline for help and support, see *aims.org.uk/rights*.

If you want to have a caesarean instead

Your right to choose a caesarean is covered in detail on page 100. Some women decide that a caesarean birth is preferable to an induced labour, and it is quite reasonable to request a caesarean instead. You can also ask to have a caesarean if you have started the induction process but are not happy with how it is progressing. If that's what you would prefer, ask to be referred to an obstetrician to explain your preferences. The same suggestions for successfully requesting an induction, discussed above, can be used when requesting a caesarean.

You can read more information about caesarean birth on the AIMS Birth Information pages on our website, or in the book, *Caesarean Birth – your questions answered*. See *aims.org.uk/rights*.

Summary

This chapter explains why 'due dates' are so problematic. Usually, babies are born when they are ready, and a longer than average pregnancy is perfectly normal. Inducing labour has risks and sometimes has benefits, and it is important to understand these so that you can make an informed decision. Remember that if you do decide to be induced, you can use your knowledge of how birth works to make it as positive and as likely to succeed as possible, particularly by considering your birth environment, and by staying as mobile as possible. Most importantly, the decision about whether or not to accept the offer of induction is yours.

Chapter 9

Your rights during your birth

Rights to accept or decline treatment and interventions

Provided you have legal capacity (see Chapter 1 p.7), you have the right to decide whether to accept or decline all treatment and interventions during your birth. Nothing is obligatory. As we have said before, a midwife or doctor has no more right to put their fingers in your vagina than you have to put your fingers into one of their body orifices. Only if you agree – and agreement must be because you have been given the pros and cons of each test or intervention offered and you have decided that, on balance, it's right for you – only then can the intervention happen.

Making decisions about interventions while in labour

When you are in labour, there is still only one person who can make decisions about what you will allow to happen to you, and that's *you* (I know, I've mentioned this a lot before!). There is no doubt that when you are in labour, decisions can be harder to make. Not only are there the sensations or pains of labour to be considered, but our brains change state in labour and this sometimes makes it harder to communicate. It doesn't mean that we are less able to think or compute; in fact, most birthing women and people are very focused, but turning thoughts into words can be harder. Caregivers should therefore only talk between contractions, and support you to have more time to think and respond.

This is a reminder that no matter what's happening, you can ask for the benefits and risks of what is being suggested, and what alternatives there might be. Check in with your intuition – what do YOU feel? And finally, what will happen if you do nothing (or wait a while). This can be a helpful way of handling unexpected twists in labour. Don't forget the BRAIN acronym (see page 31 for a full explanation):

Benefits

Risks

Alternatives

Intuition

Nothing

The downside of this approach is that it does mean that you need to engage the part of your brain that processes information. The hormones of labour suppress this part of the brain as a part of helping us to cope with labour. We are generally able to 'come out' of this changed brain state if we need to listen and make decisions, but doing so may change your ability to cope with labour for a while. If you are aware of this, you might find that you suddenly feel less in control or in more pain – but this doesn't happen to everyone. Knowing that this can be the case means that, if you do experience it, you will be aware of the need to allow your body to relax back into your labour afterwards. It is much easier to do this if you are feeling safe and supported, which is why the way that the people around you act is so important.

If a person is trying to talk to you while you are having a contraction, you might want to tell them, or signal to them, to wait until it passes, so that you can focus on the contraction, and then on them if and when you are ready.

Sometimes you will be asked the same question multiple times, even if you've made a decision to decline what is being offered. This might be something like offering a routine vaginal exam, being asked to lie on the bed to help with monitoring, or something like being told that you should have the assistance of forceps. If you are sure that declining this at this time is right for you, you can state this very clearly and tell them not to ask again unless something changes. You might prefer to state that you will reconsider in a period of time, if you are willing to do so.

For example:

Midwife: "I'm just going to pop my fingers inside to see how dilated you are."

Birthing person: "My birth plan says no internal exams unless medically necessary. Why do you want to?"

Midwife: "Well it's ok, don't worry, we just need to check you, that's all."

Birthing person: "Is there a medical need for this?"

Midwife: "Well, yes, there's a reason for everything we do. We just want a healthy mother and baby."

Birthing person: "So what do you need to do this for?"

Midwife: "Because the guidelines say we need to do this every four hours."

Birthing person: "Is there a particular medical need for me right now?"

Midwife: "Well, not as such."

Birthing person: "In that case I'm going to say no, thank you. Please don't ask me again unless there's a specific medical need."

Your rights to an active birth

As already mentioned in Chapter 7 (p.81), you are more likely to have a positive, straightforward vaginal birth if you move as your body wishes while you are labouring. Your baby's position guides your body to move and sway in order to support your baby in the best way to move through your pelvis. When a movement or position reduces your pain this is because you are listening to the feedback from your body about what it needs to best support your birth.

You can use any space in the room you're in (or leave it and find another space) as you wish. Lean over a table, chair, shelf (if it's strong enough!), the bed. Hang onto someone. Use a birthing ball or ceiling sling. Kneel on the bed leaning over the back rest. Remember that hospital beds can be raised and lowered to a good leaning height! Squat, if you can! Walk if it feels right. Sway.

You may be asked to get onto the bed to be monitored. Intermittent monitoring (if you accept it) can easily be done with you in any position. If you accept continuous monitoring, you may be asked to lie still on the bed so as not to lose the trace of the baby. There is no evidence that continuous monitoring leads to better outcomes compared to intermittent monitoring, and there is evidence that it causes harm. One problem with it is that it is trying to monitor a baby's heart rate while the baby is in one position, but the point of labour is for the baby to move somewhere else! By asking women to stay still on the bed in order to keep the connection with the baby, the woman is being asked to ignore her body when it's trying to birth her baby. You can read more about this on the AIMS Birth Information page, 'Monitoring your baby's heartbeat in labour' at *aims.org.uk/rights*.

If you decide to accept continuous monitoring you don't need to stay on the bed. Not lying still might mean that the monitor needs frequent readjustment, or it might need a birth companion to hold the equipment in place. You may experience a lot of pressure to lie on the bed, but you don't have to.

Your right to pain relief

The right to access pain relief is covered by international law as well as the European Convention on Human Rights, which outlaws what is described as "inhuman and degrading treatment". Under these laws – and simple human compassion – we should all be able to access a variety of pain-relieving options in our labour should that be the right decision for us. While some drugs may not be appropriate for medical reasons, for instance some people have serious reactions to opiates, generally speaking no form of pain relief, pharmaceutical or otherwise, should be denied to women or people who want it. The decision to accept or decline pain relief should be based on the individual's own wishes, and what's right for them. We all have the right to decide what is best for us, and there should be no taboo in planning no pain relief, or some, or lots of pain relief in labour.

A well-supported woman or person giving birth with people she trusts in an environment that supports her body to labour well is less likely to need pharmaceutical pain relief than women who feel scared, alone or who do not trust the people around her. Therefore, the most important thing that all pregnant women and people can plan for is to create the most positive birth environment that they can. See Chapter 7 (p.81) for more information about this.

Sometimes, birthing women and people need more help with pain, for instance, if the baby isn't yet in a good position for birth, or during induction of labour as the body's own pain relief systems are less likely to be as effective as they are in a spontaneous labour.

All forms of pharmaceutical pain relief (drugs) carry risks and possible side effects and, in various ways, they can interfere with labour and lead to an increased chance of interventions or problems, such as the need for assistance with forceps or the baby being sleepy and hard to feed after birth. This is one reason why many pregnant women and people decide to explore drug-free pain relief options such as birth pools, TENS machines, massage and hypnotherapy. These forms of pain relief and comfort will not be right for everyone, nor will they work for everyone, and for some the pain of labour may be more than they can tolerate. Equally, pharmaceutical pain relief can be positive for labour if it allows a woman or person to rest or reduces the chance of trauma. It is therefore imperative that effective pharmaceutical pain relief is available and that women are supported in their right to use it.

Epidurals
An epidural can only be performed by an anaesthetist and they are normally only available in the obstetric unit, and never at home – and sometimes even in hospital there isn't an anaesthetist available to give epidurals to all women who want one.

Epidurals are usually an extremely effective form of pain relief, although some women find that they do not work or only work in one part of their body. They may be medically more suited to being given later in labour rather than in the early stages, because giving them too early can interfere with labour and are more likely to lead to complications or interventions. Having said that, epidurals can lead to complications whenever they are used, so knowing their risks and benefits in advance is important. You should ask for and be provided with information about the risks and benefits of all forms of available pain relief in advance of labour to make it easier for you to make a decision on the day.

Relief from pain is a human right, and if, after being given an explanation of the possible risks and benefits you still wish to have epidural pain relief, you should be given it, no matter how far through your labour you are.

Opiates

Opiates, which include pethidine, meptid and diamorphine (medical grade heroin) can reduce pain for some women, but for others just leave them feeling out of control. Some women have reported that they were more susceptible to coercion after being given opiate drugs. These drugs can sometimes negatively affect the baby by making them sleepy, which can cause problems during labour or with the babies breathing at birth, which may necessitate giving another drug to the baby to counteract the effects of the opiate given to the mother. Another issue is that it may make it harder for the baby to feed after birth. However, for some women and birthing people they are a blessed relief, allowing rest and recuperation and the ability to prepare for the next stage of their labour. Because of the risks to both mother and baby, opiates are normally only available in the hospital's obstetric unit and some birth centres, although some women have been able to access them at home, with prior planning.

Entonox™ (Gas and air)

'Gas and air' is gas called nitrous oxide and is commonly known by its brand name Entonox. It is normally available to everyone who gives birth, no matter where they are, as long as midwives are in attendance. It should not be removed from you if you want to continue to use it unless there is a genuine medical reason. If you are transferring from one ward to another, or from the labour room to theatre, you can ask for a portable unit to take with you. Note that some women feel that after having used gas and air they felt more susceptible to coercion.

Non-pharmaceutical pain relief

The right to pain relief also applies to non-pharmaceutical pain relief such as birth pools, and it is not acceptable for women to be told that they cannot labour or birth in water solely because they are labelled 'high risk' when the risk itself would not be affected by water. Even then, reasonable adjustments should be made to support pregnant women to access water should they wish to. For instance, women having a vaginal birth after a previous caesarean (VBAC) should have access to a pool if they want to. Continuous monitoring may be recommended and, if the woman accepts it, appropriate equipment should be available to support this option.

Similarly, women should not be denied access to the water because they have a high BMI, or limited mobility, but instead appropriate equipment should be put into place to ensure that all women and birthing people can access a pool if they wish. You can read more about this in Chapter 7 (p.81).

For more information about ways of managing your labour, see the AIMS Birth Information page at *aims.org.uk/rights*.

Eating and drinking

It used to be the case (and still is in some countries) that women and birthing people were told that they were not 'allowed' to eat or drink in labour. This is because there was a concern that if a caesarean was required under general anaesthetic, the woman could aspirate any vomit. However, this complication is extremely rare with modern anaesthetic skills and drugs. It is not unusual for people to be put under anaesthetic when they have recently eaten – for instance after road accidents – and dealing with this is considered to be a normal part of care.

Not eating or drinking in labour means that you are undertaking something that is hugely energetic without topping up your body's resources. It's important to go with what your body tells you and eat and drink if you feel like it. As labour progresses you may feel much less like eating, but drinks which help to give you energy, or a teaspoon of honey, can be very helpful to give your body the boost and support that it needs. Keeping hydrated is also important, and regular sips of drinks, possibly with a straw, are probably easier than trying to drink a lot in one go.

Remember that it is your body, and if you want to eat or drink, no one can stop you. If there is a really good medical reason to not eat or drink you will be told this, and *you* can make *your* decision from there.

Vaginal examinations

A vaginal exam (VE) is usually an examination of your cervix to see how dilated it is, but might also include a check of other things, such as your baby's position, judged by the feel of the bones of their head. Some women and people don't mind VEs at all, some find them uncomfortable and some find them extremely painful. For some people VEs are traumatic. VEs can lead to a higher chance of infection, and this risk rises with the number that are done.

It is extremely important to know that no one may put their fingers in your vagina for any reason without your permission, whether it's for a check of your cervix, a sweep, to feel your baby, to screw a sensor into your baby's head to monitor their heart, to take a sample of your baby's blood from their scalp or any of the many other reasons they offer. It is also not permissible for a woman to consent to a VE and then be given a sweep without her permission – this is criminal assault and battery. You, and only you can decide whether you are going to allow access to your vagina. One more time: **no one can put their fingers in your vagina without your consent.** A midwife or doctor has no right to do this unless you give your informed consent.

Sometimes, women or people are told that they have to have a VE in order to obtain certain health care, such as access to the labour ward, a birth pool, gas and air or an epidural. This is untrue. It is a breach of our legal human rights to withhold pain relief. To force a woman to accept a VE in order to obtain medical care is a criminal assault as she is not giving her permission freely for a person to enter her vagina, but instead is being coerced.

It might be that the VE could give information that is valuable for decision making. For instance, if a woman is really suffering with pain, and wants an epidural, but she is very early on in her labour and only 1cm dilated, the epidural may inhibit her labour and lead to interventions that may not otherwise have happened. However, being just 1 or 2cm dilated does not mean that a person is definitely in early labour, as a VE does not give any information on how long labour will take to progress. We can be at 1cm for 30 minutes and 9cm for many hours. The cervix does not open in a linear manner, meaning that if, say, you've dilated 1cm in an hour, it doesn't mean that it will take another hour for each remaining centimetre.

More information is available on the AIMS website to help you to make a decision about having a VE. See *aims.org.uk/rights*.

If you agree to a VE you have a right to decide who carries this out and that may include requesting a person of a specific gender. If no one is available that you feel comfortable with, you may be faced with accepting someone you are not comfortable with or declining the VE. If you wish to have a chaperone during an examination, one must be provided for you, and this is likely to be a midwife or doctor. You can ask for a chaperone whether or not the healthcare provider who has offered to undertake the procedure is the same gender as you.

Forceps and ventouse (sometimes called instrumental delivery)

Sometimes, women and birthing people will be offered forceps or a ventouse to assist with their birth. Forceps are rather like large, open spoons which are placed either side of your baby's head inside your vagina, and are used to help to rotate or pull on your baby. A ventouse is a suction cap which is stuck (by vacuum) to the top of your baby's head. The forceps or ventouse are pulled at the same time as the birthing woman or person is pushing. You are quite likely to need an episiotomy (a cut into your perineum) if you have forceps, although this is less likely with the ventouse. Some doctors are more skilled than others in using forceps without doing an episiotomy. Sometimes forceps or ventouse can be helpful if a baby is in a position which may mean it is hard for them to be born. They may also be used when there is a need for the baby to be born quickly if they are showing signs of distress. If it is being offered just because of the position of your baby you may be able to try some different birthing positions to help the baby to rotate or move before resorting to an instrumental birth.

The Miles Circuit can help babies to get into a better position for birth, and the Spinning Babies website has useful information on optimising a baby's position in the womb. See *aims.org.uk/rights*.

Forceps and ventouse can both sometimes cause short- and long-term injuries to both mother and baby and so you may want to find out about them in advance of birth. This can help you to understand the benefits and risks with more time to consider them. Having an instrumental birth may mean that a caesarean birth can be avoided but some people decide that they would prefer a caesarean, instead of attempting an instrumental birth.

As with all interventions, even though the wording used may not make it sound like an offer, you can decline this intervention if you wish.

You might not have a lot of time, but you will almost always have a few minutes, and often much longer, before having to make a decision. Options will usually include waiting longer for baby to be born without instruments, or going straight to a caesarean if you prefer. Remember, if you are told that you 'have to' have instrumental assistance, the decision is still yours, and yours alone. If you decline it and then feel that actually it's the best thing for you, you can change your mind.

Making decisions about your caesarean

If you have a caesarean birth, whether planned before labour or not, you still have rights. Having a caesarean birth plan can be really helpful even if you're planning a vaginal birth, as this can help to ensure that you have the time to think about what is important to you. There is more information in Chapter 7 (p.81) about planning a caesarean birth.

A caesarean birth is still your birth. Communicate your wishes with your caregivers and do feel free to negotiate.

The book *Caesarean Birth – your questions answered* is a great reference book when creating a caesarean birth plan, and the link below includes references to many useful resources. You can find it on our website at *aims.org.uk/rights*.

Summary

Our bodies are our own. No one has the right to make any decisions about what happens to our bodies other than us – including when we are giving birth. Understanding what medical care may be offered to us, and thinking about it in advance of birth can help us to make decisions about what is right for us before we are in a situation where decisions may be harder to make. In all but the most severe medical emergencies there is time to wait, to see what happens or to just think things through before making your decision and no matter what, provided you retain capacity (see Chapter 1, p.7), if you decide that you do not want an intervention, it would be illegal for anyone to perform it.

Chapter 10

After your baby is born

Cutting the umbilical cord

After your baby is born, the effect of air on the cord starts a process that collapses the vein and arteries in the cord, and during this time the cord goes from thick and purple to thin and white. This may take anything from a few minutes to an hour or even more. The blood that is in the cord and placenta is pushed into the baby, and this can be as much as a third of their blood volume, so it is very important that they get it.

From around the 1970s until quite recently, it was normal practice to clamp and cut the umbilical cord immediately after birth, which cuts off the baby from their own blood. We now know that this lead to anaemia and other health problems. See *aims.org.uk/rights*.

We are seeing a change in practice with more of a delay before this is done. Waiting until the placenta and cord have finished their job and then clamping and cutting the cord is known as 'optimal cord clamping', or 'wait for white' because the cord goes from a deep purple colour to a grey-white when all of the blood has flowed from the placenta to the baby. Another term, 'delayed cord clamping' is often used intermittently with 'optimal cord clamping' but is generally considered to mean leaving the cord for a few minutes, but not necessarily until all of the blood has passed to the baby. In many cases there is concern that although cord clamping is being delayed, it is still being done too soon, particularly at caesarean births, or if a baby is distressed.

If, after a vaginal birth, your baby needs help with breathing, in most cases it is possible to help without cutting the cord. Leaving the cord attached is even more important when your baby is taking longer than expected to breathe, as he or she will usually still be getting some oxygen and blood through the cord, and research has shown that this leads to higher oxygenation of the brain, and higher blood pressure. Cutting the cord cuts off this supply of oxygen. However, not all doctors or midwives are trained or confident in resuscitating a baby next to their mother and with the cord intact. Some hospitals have resuscitation tables that can be use alongside a mother which make this process easier. In this situation you might decide that you will allow the healthcare provider to cut the cord so that they can work in the way that they feel comfortable. In reality, in most cases the doctor or midwife caring for you will simply cut the cord without asking you so if this is important to you, you may need to be very clear and vocal about your decisions.

You may want a discussion with your midwife in advance of your birth to make your preferences clear. Any agreements about care can be marked in your birth plan, and, if you can, tell each healthcare provider that attends your birth of your decision.

If your baby is born by caesarean and you are both well you should be able to have delayed cord clamping. However, there will be more time pressure to clamp and cut the cord than there would be in a vaginal birth, so the delay may be only be a minute or two – although you can certainly ask for more. If your baby is unwell and in need of treatment after birth, the cord will usually be clamped and cut, and your baby will be checked over and, if necessary, treated by a paediatrician. Depending on what treatment is required it may be possible to use a bedside resuscitation table if one is available, but there are very few doctors who are trained to do this in a caesarean birth. You should be supported in making decisions about cutting the cord and your baby accessing treatment so if this is important to you it is worth talking to your doctor about it before the caesarean, if you have time to, although if you feel able to, you can make your wishes known during the caesarean.

Read more about the research into optimal cord clamping at *aims.org.uk/rights*.

Clamping the umbilical cord

Most babies' cords are long enough to allow the baby to be cuddled skin to skin with their mother or birth parent after a vaginal birth, if both are well enough to do so, without having to cut the cord. Some babies have cords which are too short for this, so it is up to you whether you are happy just to have your baby on your tummy until the cord is white and has stopped pulsating, or whether you have it cut earlier in order to be able to hold your baby to your chest more easily.

When the cord is cut, two plastic cord clamps will normally be attached and the cord cut between them. You can decide who you want to cut the cord. The plastic clamp nearest to your baby is left attached to the remaining short amount of cord. A few days later the cord, and the clamp attached, will fall off.

This plastic clamp is quite big, and some parents find that it interferes with skin to skin contact with their baby, and can be uncomfortable when breastfeeding. Parents can choose another method to close off the cord if they wish. Two of the options are a cord tie or a cord ring. A tie is simply a piece of thread – often chain crocheted or plaited cotton embroidery thread – that is tied firmly around the cord, ensuring that the ends of the tie are as short as possible to minimise the risk of the cord wrapping itself tight around your baby's genitals and causing an injury. The cord stump and tie should be kept outside the top of the nappy, just as with a plastic clip. Another option is a cord ring, which is a tiny special elastic band attached with a specific tool, available from specialist midwifery suppliers.

If the cord is left to become completely white before cutting, most babies don't need the cord clamping or tying off. However, rarely the cord can start to bleed again so it is a good idea to have either a clamp, cord tie or the specialist band to keep it tied off until the cord drops off naturally.

Lotus birth

A lotus birth is where the parents decide not to cut the baby's cord at all, but keep the placenta and cord attached to the baby until it falls off naturally, within a few days. The placenta is usually washed and wrapped, and preserved with salt and herbs or by other methods, to reduce the chance of bacterial growth.

You have the right to lotus birth if you wish, whether you have a vaginal or caesarean birth, and this should be supported unless there is a clear medical need not to. You will need to clearly instruct your midwife or doctor to not cut the cord at all, and you will probably need to remind them, or have a birth companion do so, at the moment of birth and in the time thereafter.

Birthing your placenta

After your baby is born you will need to birth your placenta. This is sometimes called the third stage, or the third stage of labour, and is normally defined as the time following your baby's birth up until you birth your placenta.

Deciding whether to have a 'physiological' or 'managed' placenta birth

Most women are offered an injection of artificial oxytocin straight after birth, which can help your placenta to be born more quickly, and may reduce your chance of a heavy bleed. Sometimes other drugs, or combinations of drugs, are offered, especially if you are bleeding heavily. Once the placenta has separated the cord is gently pulled (cord traction), sometimes with pressure put on the top of your uterus (by pressing your belly), to ease the placenta out.

This process is known as having a 'managed third stage' or sometimes 'active management of the placenta', and if you are having an induced labour with artificial oxytocin it is likely that this process will be necessary. Your body may not have released the same amount of natural oxytocin as it would if you had experienced a spontaneous labour, so the additional artificial oxytocin may be needed to help your uterus to continue to contract.

A managed third stage can reduce the time it takes to birth your placenta, and it can reduce the amount of blood that you lose immediately after birth, but there are risks from the drugs and the management process. Risks from the drugs include the fact that some women feel very unwell and can vomit after having them, blood pressure can go down and post birth contractions (afterpains) can become more painful. Breastfeeding may also be impacted, with fewer women breastfeeding after two and six weeks compared to those who did not have the drugs. See *aims.org.uk/rights*.

Other risks of active management include pain from the cord traction and from the pressure on the abdomen, and, very rarely, injury to the uterus. For a comprehensive discussion of the risks and benefits of management of the placenta birth, please refer to the AIMS book about birthing your placenta available from *aims.org.uk/rights*.

You may prefer not to have this intervention, and instead choose to birth your placenta without drugs or assistance (physiological third stage). This works best when our bodies are supported to release their own oxytocin. Remember that oxytocin release is highest when we feel comfortable, safe and loved, ideally with dimmed lighting and a calm and peaceful environment (see Chapter 7 p.81 for more information on oxytocin).

It is very important that no one attempts to pull on the cord during a physiological placenta birth unless it is very clear that the placenta has separated, as doing this can trigger a serious bleed, called a postpartum haemorrhage (PPH). You can read more about PPHs on the AIMS Birth Information pages at *aims.org.uk/rights*.

If you decide to have a physiological placenta birth, but at any point decide to change your mind, you can do this. You can choose to have the injection at any time (at which stage the active management processes can happen).

These suggestions can all help your placenta to be born:

- Holding your baby skin to skin, and if you want to, allowing your baby to nuzzle and, if they are ready, suckle at the breast. This is an excellent way to release oxytocin.
- Change position – gravity helps. Try standing up if you can, or squatting, or just getting up on all fours if you are lying down.
- Passing urine (some women find a catheter helpful if they are struggling to pass urine and their bladder is very full).
- Sitting on the toilet (this is both a good position for the placenta to be born, and it also helps to pass urine).

Rights to your placenta

The placenta belongs to the person who gives birth to it. Most people decide to leave it for the midwives to dispose of, but some people decide that they want to keep it.

Some choose to consume some or all of their placenta in a smoothie, by eating small amounts after birth in various ways, or may have it dried and put into capsules or made into a homeopathic tincture.

Other people choose to bury their placenta, perhaps in an important place in the garden. The placenta is not considered to be 'bodily remains' and therefore you can bury it at home if you want to, although you may wish to check with your local council to see if there are any regulations that you should know about, and avoid burying it near a water source, stream or river. There are many different things that people do with their placenta, and this is covered in detail in the AIMS book about birthing yout placenta – see *aims. org.uk/rights*.

The 'Golden Hour'

Special time with your baby

'The Golden Hour' refers to the time immediately after birth where you and your baby or babies, together with anyone else that you wish to have with you, should be left to get to know one another without being disturbed unnecessarily. If both mother and baby are well, and do not need immediate, urgent medical care then it is important that midwives and doctors support the family to have this time together without unnecessary interference.

This is a time when the instinctive responses of mother or birth parent and baby start building a bond outside the womb. It is an important time for breastfeeding initiation, and the high levels of oxytocin that this triggers helps to reduce bleeding from the uterus. Skin to skin contact and breast suckling helps the baby's microbiome to be colonised with beneficial bacteria. The mother or birthing person's instincts are often to explore their baby, to get to know them as a new, precious person, often together with their partner, if they have one. It is important that midwives and doctors support parents' privacy at this time so that they do not feel 'watched' as this can interfere with these instincts.

You do not have to hand your baby to anyone during this time (or ever!), and if you wish to have your baby weighed and measured you can decide to wait until you are ready. When deciding whether to give consent to be separated from your baby, even for a short time, these are important considerations.

The term 'Golden Hour' is a little prescriptive. It doesn't have to be an hour. However, the reason that the hour is suggested is that it takes, on average, about 45 minutes for babies to latch to the breast (in which case an hour may be too short!).

For some people, the birth means that this time together isn't possible. This might be because the mother or birth parent is unwell or recovering from a general anaesthetic, or the baby needs treatment of a type which cannot be done next to the mother or birth parent. This can be deeply distressing, so it is important that as soon as mother or birth parent and baby are both well enough, they are supported to have as much time together as they wish. Even if it's a long time (sometimes days or weeks) after birth, the value of spending this time together can't be overstated.

Feeding your baby

After birth, your body is still your own and only you get to make the decision about what happens to it. This includes the decision about whether or not you want to breastfeed. If you decide that you do want to breastfeed then this is your right. If you decide that you want to formula feed, it is your right to make this decision too. If you prefer to mix feed (part formula, part breastmilk), this is also a decision that only you can make. Before making this decision you may wish to research breastfeeding and formula feeding and how they each influence your health and the health of your baby or babies, but you don't have to.

The postnatal ward

Some hospitals permit partners to stay with women on the postnatal ward; others do not. You can ask your hospital what their policy is, and if they say no to your partner staying, you can find out whether this might be possible in a private room. Not everyone will want their partner to stay with them, but many people want to have someone to help them and find being separated from their partner, and their partner being separated from their baby, very distressing. At the same time, consideration for those who feel uncomfortable about partners being on the ward when they are extremely vulnerable is important. There is no specific right for your partner to stay with you on the hospital premises, but clearly your baby is their child too, and being separated from them can be really upsetting and sometimes traumatic. Your partner being respectful of the shared space and using only the facilities provided for them means that it is more likely that they will be permitted to stay. Empathic discussion, negotiation and persistence can sometimes work wonders.

Unfortunately, because of the pressures on postnatal services, which tend to be less well funded and often short staffed, you may need to be quite insistent about the care you need on the postnatal ward. This can be extremely tough if you are also unwell yourself, so thinking in advance about different ways to advocate for yourself might be helpful.

First, being empathic and understanding of the fact that the staff are likely to be very stretched is important. You can use phrases like, "I know you're very busy; I'm just wondering how you can help me with XYZ" shows them that you're thinking of them, but also be clear about what you are asking for. Instead of "Are there any breast pumps available?" consider saying, "Please can you get me a breast pump?".

Do remember that hospital is not a prison and you may leave at any time, if you want to. You do not need to have been discharged, nor to sign any paperwork unless you want to. See the section below, 'Leaving the hospital after birth'.

Vitamin K

The decision about whether or not to give your baby vitamin K after birth is made by the people with parental rights, not the doctors or midwives. It is often offered soon after birth, so it is something you may want to think about before your baby is born. If you decide to give your baby vitamin K, you can wait until you are ready, it does not need to be given until you have spent as much time as you like together with your baby.

If you would like more information about vitamin K and your options, see the AIMS Birth Information page 'Vitamin K and your newborn baby' at *aims.org.uk/rights*.

The Newborn and Infant Physical Examination (NIPE)

All babies are offered a set of tests after birth to look at their eyes, heart, hips and if your baby is a boy, testicles. If you birth in hospital or a birth centre and you don't want to wait for it to be done before you leave, you don't have to. You can arrange for it to be done later, by bringing your baby back to hospital, or some GPs can do it at their surgery. Some community or independent midwives are also trained in doing the NIPE test so they can do it at home if you arrange it with them.

If your baby is born at home then your community midwife should be able to advise you on how to access this test, but if you want to avoid going into hospital you can ask for a midwife with NIPE training to do it at your home.

The NIPE Test is offered within 72 hours of birth and then again at between 6-8 weeks. You may experience pressure to have this test within this time because there is a payment made to the provider (meaning the GP surgery or hospital) who does it, but it can be done outside of these times.

However, sometimes the NIPE Test picks up problems which do require urgent treatment, for instance heart conditions, which is why it is offered soon after birth.

You don't need to accept the offer of this test, or you can accept parts of it but not others, or you can accept the whole thing – the decision is with the person or people with parental responsibility. The midwife or doctor who does the test must obtain consent to do it.

For more information on the NIPE Test, see the NHS website via *aims.org.uk/rights.*

Leaving the hospital after birth

If you go to hospital for any treatment during your pregnancy, or for your labour, your birth or after your birth, you can leave at any time if you wish. Hospital is not a prison and you do not have to wait to be discharged. You do not need to sign any document to say that you are discharging yourself, even if it is against medical advice, unless you want to. You might wish to listen to the advice of the medical staff before you decide whether or not you want to leave, but if you feel that this is of no value to you, you can go. Note that some hospitals tag babies with security devices which set off an alarm if you try to leave without it being removed. This is to reduce the chance of babies being kidnapped from the ward, not to stop parents from leaving with their own baby. Hospitals must remove these tags from babies if asked by a person with parental responsibility (in the absence of a court order saying otherwise).

If your baby is offered treatment and you do not agree with it, you can still legally leave with your baby. However, staff do have a responsibility to ensure the safeguarding of the children in their care. While it would be illegal for a midwife, doctor or other healthcare professional to coerce you into accepting treatment for your child by threatening a referral to Children's Services, it is expected that parents will carefully consider care that is offered, and if it is declined a safeguarding referral may be made.

It is therefore advisable to be very clear about your understanding of what treatment is offered and the benefits and risks of it before you make a decision to consent to or decline it. Unless there's an emergency which cannot wait, you also have the right to have the time to make your decision about what is right for your baby.

If you are facing a referral to Children's Services we would advise you to seek legal advice immediately. The Family Rights Group is a charity which has a helpline staffed by lawyers who specialise in supporting families through referrals to Children's Services. You can also seek help and support from the AIMS helpline. See *aims.org.uk/rights*.

Hospital treatment post birth for you or your baby or babies

If you require hospital treatment

If you need to be in hospital straight after your birth, you should be able to keep your baby with you if you want. You should be fully supported to do this whether or not you are breastfeeding, but if for any reason you cannot have your baby with you and you want to breastfeed, you should be supported with expressing and storing your milk, and you can ask for a hospital grade electric pump. Colostrum (the first milk that your body produces) is usually more easily expressed by hand than with a breast pump, so if you need help learning how to hand express, ask your midwife, and remember that you are also entitled to support from the hospital's breastfeeding specialists. (See Chapter 2 p.13, Infant Feeding Specialists.)

If you are told that you are unable to breastfeed due to a medical drug that you are taking, you can ask whether there's another drug that is safe to use. You can also check with The Breastfeeding Network's *Drugs in Breastmilk*

Information Service as many drugs which are not licensed for breastfeeding can still be safely used. See *aims.org.uk/rights*.

If your baby is unwell, and separated from you in a special baby care ward such as the Neonatal Intensive Care Unit (NICU) or the Special Care Baby Unit (SCBU), you should be given support to see your baby if you are well enough to go. You might need to advocate for yourself, or have someone there to advocate for your needs – for instance, getting a wheelchair to take you to your baby if you need one; planning how to safely leave the ward to go to your baby's ward if you have particular medical needs; ensuring that you don't miss ward rounds, medication rounds and food provision in your own ward if you leave it to visit your baby. Speak to the midwife who is caring for you to ensure that you know when you need to be back, or what can be done if you miss care that you need, or a meal.

If your baby is unwell after birth, or if they are born with a condition or disability it is likely to be hard to remember your rights and sometimes parents can feel bulldozed by being told what they have to do. Remember, your baby or babies are yours, and you can ask questions, and have the time you need to make decisions yourself on behalf of your child or children. You are central to the care team for your baby.

If your baby requires hospital treatment

It is really important not to underestimate how stressful having a baby or babies in SCBU or NICU is, because while they're in the thick of it many people just put one foot in front of the other and don't think too much about how they feel. It can affect how you feel about negotiating what you need as there may be little 'brain space' left. However, focusing on some of the basics is a good start. For instance, it's unusual for parents to be able to stay in hospital with their babies if the birth parent has been discharged. However, most NICUs and SCBUs have a 24 hours visitor policy for parents. You might be encouraged to leave, but you don't have to, and you can stay as long as you want to even if you are strongly encouraged to go home.

Most (although not all) premature and many sick babies benefit from kangaroo care – ongoing skin to skin contact – especially with their birth parent but also with partners and others. Kangaroo care has been shown to increase brain development, support breastmilk production, regulate temperature and blood sugars in the baby, improve weight gain, calm the baby and many other benefits. See *aims.org.uk/rights*.

Parents sometimes find that the nurses caring for their baby or babies want to limit the time that parents hold them. There may be good reasons for this but often it's because the nurses feel that they need to watch over babies when they're not in an incubator, and they may just not have time for this. Feel free to ask questions and ask the staff what to look for on the monitors if you are holding your baby so that you have more information about whether or not your baby can continue to be held. If you feel that your baby is well enough to be held, and you are both benefiting from it, but you are still being told not to, you can ask for a second opinion.

One of the key ways to get through the challenges of having your baby in NICU or SCBU is getting support from others. You could contact Bliss, a national charity for parents of babies who are born prematurely or unwell – see *aims.org.uk/rights*.

You might also find a local doula who has experience in this area, which is especially helpful if they have knowledge of local guidelines.

Breastmilk and babies in NICU or SCBU

All babies benefit from breastmilk, but for premature babies, or those who are unwell, breastmilk can be especially important. Breastmilk contains unique components which directly support the immune system, and help babies to recover from illness. We also know that giving formula to premature babies leads to a higher chance of a serious illness called necrotising enterocolitis (NEC), which can lead to bowel damage and can be fatal. A reference from UNICEF states:

> 'A total of 926 preterm infants were studied, 51 of whom developed NEC. Exclusively formula-fed infants were 6 to 10 times more likely to develop NEC than those who received breastmilk. Although NEC is rare in babies over 30 weeks gestation, it was 20 times more common if the baby had received no breastmilk.'
> See *aims.org.uk/rights*.

Protection against NEC is highest in babies who only receive breastmilk, and the risk of NEC is highest for babies who are only fed formula, with babies who are fed some breastmilk and some formula having some protection from the breastmilk that they are given, but not as much as those who are only fed breastmilk.

If you want your baby to only receive breastmilk, be extremely clear about this. Ensure this is in your baby's notes and that you do not consent to them being given formula. You might want to tape a note onto their cot, or if it can be safely done, their incubator, and tell each of your baby's caregivers.

You should be given support to breastfeed in the hospital, or to express and safely store your milk, and, if necessary, to get access to donor breastmilk from a milk bank which adheres to the national guidelines. Donor breastmilk is donated by women who have been screened for milk-borne illnesses, and the milk itself is then screened and processed for safety. Donor breastmilk should be available to premature and sick babies whose mothers cannot provide sufficient breastmilk for their baby or babies' needs. Donor breastmilk from an official milk bank is screened and pasteurised and despite being processed still reduces the chance of a baby contracting NEC, although isn't quite as protective as mother's own unprocessed milk. Formula fed babies are twice as likely to contract NEC as babies fed processed donor breastmilk from a milk bank. Cochrane has a useful review on donor breastmilk and NEC – see *aims. org.uk/rights*.

Breastfeeding support in hospital may be good, but sometimes it isn't, so you might need or prefer to access external support. Try contacting one of the four UK breastfeeding charities, Association of Breastfeeding Mothers (ABM), Breastfeeding Network (BfN), La Leche League (LLL) and NCT. For support with accessing donor breastmilk if your hospital isn't being supportive, try the milk bank charity UKAMB. Another important organisation is the Human Milk Foundation which supports families to access donor milk, provides lactation support and researches breastmilk and its unique properties. See *aims.org.uk/rights* for links to these organisations.

Being with your baby during treatment

Unless there is a reason why it may be dangerous for you to be with your baby during treatment (e.g. during surgery), you should be supported to be with them at all times. Many treatments can be done at the same time as you breastfeed your baby, and this has been shown to reduce their sense of pain. This includes routinely offered interventions, tests and medications such as vitamin K and the heel prick test (Guthrie test). You should be able to hold your baby for many types of treatment or tests, and doing so can help to keep them, and you, calmer. If a doctor or midwife wants to take your baby from your arms for an intervention or treatment, you can talk to them about how it can be done while you're holding them if you wish. If you are not breastfeeding your baby, holding them will still offer them comfort and help them to deal with unpleasant or painful sensations. Read more via *aims.org. uk/rights*.

Notifying and Registering the birth

Notifying the birth

A birth must be 'Notified' within 36 hours of the birth. Normally this will be done by the midwife or doctor who attends the birth, or who arrives within 6 hours of the birth, and in this case you will not have to do anything or think about this at all.

However, if a midwife or doctor is not present either at the birth or within those 6 hours post birth, then someone who was present is required by law to notify it. In this case, the AIMS Birth Information page on Freebirth has information on what is required, and how to do it. See the AIMS Birth Infodmation page, 'Freebirth, Unassisted Childbirth and Unassisted Pregnancy' at *aims.org.uk/rights*.

Registering the birth

Once a birth is notified, the process for registering your baby or babies is straightforward.

Births are registered at your nearest Registry Office. You can contact them to make an appointment; some have an online booking system. They will tell you who can register the birth given your specific circumstances. This can depend on whether the birth parent is married or not.

Summary

There are many things to consider when thinking about the time just after your baby is born, and sometimes, if the unexpected happens, we can feel very much at sea and find it harder to advocate for ourselves and for our baby or babies. Remember that as always you have the right to make decisions for you and your baby or babies (unless a court order says otherwise), You can often ask for more time to make decisions and to think about what is right for you. Having said that, if there are aspects of this part of your birth that are particularly important to you it is very advisable to talk them through with your midwife or doctor in advance, so that you can have any discussions about different points of view before you are in the more vulnerable position that birth puts us into, and have them write down their agreement in your birth plan.

The following pages offer support and information for parents whose baby has died through miscarriage or stillbirth, or soon after birth.

If you need to access this information, we are so sorry that your baby died. We hope that the following pages help you to navigate this time, and that they are supportive and informative.

There is help and support available from a variety of charities and organisations. These can be found in the Resources (p.161) near the end of this book and on the AIMS website at *aims.org.uk/rights*.

Miscarriage, stillbirth and neonatal death

Miscarriage

Definition of a miscarriage

A miscarriage is usually defined as the death of an unborn baby before the end of 23 weeks and 6 days of pregnancy. However, if a baby is born at any gestation, including before the end of 23 weeks and 6 days, and is recorded by an attending medical practitioner as showing signs of life and then dies, the baby will be registered as a live birth and recorded as a neonatal death.

If you are worried that you are having a miscarriage

Some women know that they have had a miscarriage, and others find out at a routine midwife appointment, or a scan. If you are concerned that you are having, or have had, a miscarriage you can go straight to the hospital if you want to. Some women prefer to call their GP for advice, and others prefer not to seek any medical assistance. If you feel that you would prefer to stay at home, you can, you are not obliged to go to hospital, and you can always change your mind at any time. If you do have a miscarriage, you may wish to advise your midwife, if you are booked with one, and your GP. This will ensure that the miscarriage is on your records and it will then be easier to receive appropriate care should you need it.

If there are signs of a miscarriage without symptoms of an ectopic pregnancy (read more on page 153/154 and *aims.org.uk/rights*), and if there is nothing further that can be done medically, women are generally discharged. Before this happens, the hospital should provide information about what to do if symptoms get worse, as well as advice on how to manage the process if the pregnancy does lead to a miscarriage. If a scan has not been possible, for instance if it is too early in pregnancy for a scan to give useful information, the hospital should advise when one would be possible and either arrange this or advise you how to do so via your GP or midwife. Read more here: *aims.org.uk/rights*.

This can sometimes leave pregnant women and people feeling abandoned by the system. Miscarriage charities may be able to offer support if you are in this situation. You can find more organisations which offer support after miscarriage via *aims.org.uk/rights*.

What options are available next?

If you are less than 23 weeks and 6 days pregnant, and it is confirmed that your baby has died, you can either wait until your body miscarries naturally, or induce labour with medication, or have an operation to remove the pregnancy. The Miscarriage Association has a comprehensive online booklet explaining the different options in detail. See *aims.org.uk/rights*.

There are risks and benefits to all of these options, but you should be given the choice of all of them unless there is a specific medical reason not to.

Language

Some hospital staff are used to using medical terms when they are dealing with miscarriages and might use terms like "products of conception" to mean your baby and placenta. If staff use language that you don't like, you are free to either ignore it, or request that they use terms you would prefer to hear.

Rights to tests after miscarriage

Many women and their partners are desperate to know why they had a miscarriage, but tests/investigations are usually offered only after three consecutive miscarriages or after a late miscarriage (after 14/15 weeks). This is because most people who miscarry once or twice will go on to have another pregnancy without any problem. It is unusual to offer tests to women who have suffered fewer than three miscarriages, which can be very upsetting.

You can ask for the tests to be done after one or two miscarriages, especially if you are concerned that the loss may have been caused by something preventable, but you don't have the legal right to have them. It is always worth talking to a supportive GP, though, as they may be able to arrange something for you. Sadly, it is not always possible to find a reason for recurrent miscarriage, and if a reason is found, there is not always a treatment.

There are a number of organisations which may be able to provide you with some guidance and support – see *aims.org.uk/rights*.

If you choose to go to hospital, what happens will depend on how many weeks pregnant you are, and it may also depend on what day of the week it is. For instance, at the weekend, or at night, ultrasound is not always offered immediately to women in early pregnancy who are showing signs of miscarriage. You may be offered a blood test to check your levels of pregnancy hormones, but if the routine scanning services are closed then you may not be able to access a scan unless there is a concern that the pregnancy is growing outside the uterus (an ectopic pregnancy) as this is a serious medical emergency.

The Miscarriage Association has an extremely helpful online document explaining the possible signs of miscarriage and ectopic pregnancy – see *aims.org.uk/rights*.

If there are signs of an ectopic pregnancy then it is important that you have a scan to try to determine this as it needs urgent treatment. If you are not in the hospital and you feel that you need urgent treatment, do not hesitate to call an ambulance. Please visit *aims.org.uk/rights* to links with more information on how an ectopic pregnancy may feel.

The NICE guidelines on ectopic pregnancy and miscarriage state that all maternity units should provide scanning services seven days a week, with access to the unit within 24 hours if clinically necessary. This may not always be the case, however, there will always be scanning equipment available for emergencies such as a possible ectopic pregnancy and if necessary they will call someone in to use it, if there isn't a trained sonographer on site at the time. See *aims.org.uk/rights*.

If your baby is stillborn

Definition of stillbirth

A baby who dies before birth but after 24 weeks of pregnancy, including during labour, is called a stillbirth. Stillborn babies will receive a stillbirth certificate and will require a burial or cremation by law. However, there is no specific time that this must happen by, so you can take your time and plan what is right for you.

The charity Tommy's has a helpful web page to support parents which you can find via *aims.org.uk/rights*.

Learning that your baby has died before birth, and what you may be offered

The news that your unborn baby has died is devastating, and often comes as a complete shock to parents. Rather than the plans that you had made for your baby, there will suddenly be a very different set of things to think about and decisions to make. You may be asked "What do you want to do?" when none of the options are what you want because they all relate to your baby having died, and none of the decisions are ones you want to make. It's completely normal to feel like that. Give yourself time. Usually you have time to let your options settle in your mind and allow one to come forward. Some hospitals have a bereavement team with specialist midwives who will be able to support you through the options that you have, so do ask if one is not offered to you. In the UK there are bereavement care standards which hospitals should be following. See *aims.org.uk/rights*.

If you are not already in labour, you will need to decide whether to have a vaginal birth or a caesarean. There is no specific right to have a caesarean if you want one, but it would be unlikely that you would be denied one. It is unusual for a caesarean to be offered, so if this is something that you might want to consider then you are likely to need to bring it up with your midwife yourself, and ask to be referred to a doctor to discuss the risks and benefits. Most likely, you will be advised to avoid a caesarean if possible, as they carry more risks than a vaginal birth and they can increase certain risks in future pregnancies. However, if it is right for you, then you should be able to have one. Many women report that having a vaginal birth helped them emotionally. It might help to talk to people who have been through this, or a charity like Sands, before making your decision.

If you have decided to birth vaginally, you will often be encouraged to have an induction or a caesarean rather than waiting for labour to start spontaneously. This is very likely if there is a reason for your baby to be born quickly, for instance if there are signs of infection or you have pre-eclampsia, because in some situations you may quickly become very ill. Again, the decision is yours and you can go ahead with the induction or caesarean, or decline it. If you decline the offer you can always change your mind.

If your baby dies after birth

Definition of neonatal death

When a baby is born alive at any gestation, but dies within the first four weeks after birth, this is known as a neonatal death. If you are in hospital when your baby dies, the same information below applies to you as well as to parents of stillborn babies.

You and your baby after loss

Staying with your baby

If your baby was born in hospital, or transferred to hospital after birth, you can stay with him or her as long as you wish. Equally, you don't have to stay with your baby if you don't want to. You should be given a private room and a cuddle cot, sometimes called a cold cot, which can help to protect your baby's body. Family members and friends can visit, if you wish. You can bathe, dress and hold your baby if you wish to do so, have photographs taken and hand and foot prints. If you are not sure whether you want to have photographs or prints taken, you can choose to have them done and placed into a sealed envelope to take home. Usually, hospitals provide memory boxes with special items for the family to make memories to take home.

Sometimes babies who have died are removed from their parents at birth if the baby has a medical condition that the staff feel the parents need to be prepared for. You can say that you don't want your baby to be taken away if you want to. It's your baby. Equally, if you feel you'd like some time to prepare, that's fine too.

If you want to take your baby home you can do so in most circumstances. If you wish to do this you should be provided with a cuddle cot, and information on how to take care of your baby's body until you are ready to let them go. You can bathe, dress and spend precious time with him or her.

The charity 'Sands' has very helpful information which you can access via *aims.org.uk/rights*.

Post-mortem or autopsy

A post-mortem, sometimes called an autopsy, should be offered for babies who are stillborn or die after birth. You have the right to refuse, unless it is requested by a coroner (although this is very rare). You may have questions about why your baby died and sometimes having a post-mortem will help to find out how or why they died. Unfortunately, it is common not to find a clear cause of death. In some situations, for instance if a baby has died of a specific medical condition, it might help researchers to gather information to try to prevent future deaths. Some people find that this is helpful to them, others don't. The decision in this case is entirely yours and it is important that you do not allow anyone to push you one way or another.

Burials and cremation

If your baby was born alive at any stage of pregnancy and then died (neonatal death) or if they were stillborn, they must by law be buried or cremated and their birth and death must be registered with a Registry Office.

If your baby is born before the end of 23 weeks and 6 days of pregnancy, and was not born alive, it is called a miscarriage. You can still have a funeral with a burial or cremation if you wish, but you will need a certificate from the hospital, or a GP, to say that the baby was born before 24 weeks of pregnancy. This means that if you have a miscarriage at home, you will need to take your baby to hospital, or the GP, to request this certificate, which can be very distressing. Some GPs may arrange a home visit for this, so do ask if you would prefer this option. Many hospitals will offer to arrange burial or cremation after miscarriage, though with early losses, these are likely to be shared cremations along with other babies. The hospital chaplain can often offer helpful advice.

Babies born before the end of 23 weeks and 6 days who don't show signs of life can be buried on your own property if you wish. Rules may be different for rented properties. The Miscarriage Association has a helpful and support information page – see *aims.org.uk/rights*.

Most hospitals offer a burial or cremation service free of charge, as do many crematoria. Depending on how big your baby is, they may be cremated with other babies, in which case you will not be able to have their ashes back, but you will be told where they are laid to rest. If they are cremated alone then there are sometimes enough ashes to retrieve, depending on your baby's size, but you will need to discuss this in advance.

You can also use the services of a private undertaker. There will be different options and recommendations depending on the gestation of your baby, and it is important to know what options you may have and what the consequences may be. The baby loss charity Sands, the Miscarriage Association and the Institute of Cemetery and Crematorium Management (ICCM) have created joint guidance to help. See *aims.org.uk/rights*.

Death certificates

Babies who are born at any gestation and show signs of life but then pass away are called a neonatal death, and no matter the gestation the parents of these babies should receive a death certificate.

If your baby is born outside of the hospital and no medical care provider sees that they were breathing or showing other signs of life, you can still ask for them to be registered and to receive a death certificate, although there may be some resistance to this.

For babies born after 24 weeks of pregnancy, the parents are responsible for arranging the burial or cremation of their baby, once they have the paperwork that permits them to do so. A funeral home can be very helpful, but you do not need to use one if you don't want to.

Parents of babies lost through miscarriage will not be given a death certificate. This can be upsetting, as it may feel as if the baby's short life hasn't been recognised. However, there are on-going campaigns, by charities that support parents through miscarriage and baby loss, to have all babies recognised as having been born and able to have a death certificate, no matter their gestation or whether they lived for a time after birth. The charity 'Sands' and the Miscarriage Association offer certificates that hospitals, or parents themselves, can download and complete with options for different types of families. You can access this via *aims.org.uk/rights*.

There are many organisations that help to support and care for parents who have lost their babies through miscarriage, stillbirth or soon after birth, and some of the links here may be helpful if you or someone you know is in this situation. We hope that they are helpful and we offer our deepest sympathies to you. You can find links via *aims.org.uk/rights*.

Resources

Antenatal Results and Choices: *arc-uk.org*

Association of Breastfeeding Mothers: *abm.me.uk*

Birthrights: *birthrights.org.uk*

Bliss: *bliss.org.uk*

Breastfeeding Network: *breastfeedingnetwork.org.uk*

Citizens Advice Bureau: *citizensadvice.org.uk*

Doula UK: *doula.org.uk*

Down's Syndrome Organisation: *downs-syndrome.org.uk*

Family Rights Group: frg.org.uk

Lactation Consultations Great Britain: *lcgb.org*

La Leche League: *laleche.org.uk*

Maternity Action: *maternityaction.org.uk*

Miscarriage Association: *miscarriageassociation.org.uk*

NCT: *nct.org.uk*

Positive about Down's Syndrome (PADS): *positiveaboutdownsyndrome.co.uk*

Sands: *sands.org.uk*

Soft UK: *soft.org.uk*

Together for short lives: *togetherforshortlives.org.uk*

Tommy's: *tommys.org*

'We support all maternity service users to navigate the system as it exists, and campaign for a system that truly meets the needs of all.'

AIMS Publishing

AIMS are updating their books.
Over the next two to three years, we will publish a new set of
AIMS GUIDES

You will recognise them by the splash of paint on the cover.
(See the cover of this book!)

AIMS books provide support and information for women and people in the UK who are pregnant and preparing for birth.

AIMS Guides cover a broad range of issues, from the maternity care that you can ask for to the rights that you have. The Guides are intended to be a source of vital, evidence-based and impartial information for parents and birth workers alike.

What makes AIMS books different?

- We work with a diverse and influential group of authors, and importantly we have a peer review process for our books.
- We offer extra support to our readers via the AIMS website including the Birth Information pages and Journal, and via the telephone and email Helplines.
- We know that our accessible Guides are on topics of key concern to pregnant women and people as they reflect the subjects that we are commonly asked about on the AIMS Helpline.

BUY the books at www.aims.org.uk/shop

Support AIMS by

- becoming a member, www.aims.org.uk/join-us
- by volunteering, www.aims.org.uk/volunteering
- by making a donation, www.aims.org.uk/donate

AiMS

There for your mother

Here for you

Help us to be there for your daughters

www.aims.org.uk

Twitter – @AIMS_online

Facebook – *www.facebook.com/AIMSUK*

Helpline

helpline@aims.org.uk

0300 365 0663